GETTING STARTED

BRIDGES IN MATHEMATICS

BRIDGES IN MATHEMATICS 4

written by
Allyn Fisher

illustrated by
Tyson Smith

Published by
The **MATH LEARNING CENTER**
Salem, Oregon

ISBN 9781602620070

B4TG-GS

Bridges in Mathematics Grade 4 Getting Started

The Bridges in Mathematics Grade 4 Package consists of—

Getting Started

Bridges Teachers Guide Volume One

Bridges Teachers Guide Volume Two

Bridges Teachers Guide Volume Three

Bridges Teachers Guide Volume Four

Bridges Blacklines

Bridges Overheads

Bridges Student Book Blacklines

Home Connections Blacklines

Work Place Student Book Blacklines

Student Math Journal Blacklines

Word Resource Cards

Manipulatives

Number Corner Teachers Guide Volume One

Number Corner Teachers Guide Volume Two

Number Corner Blacklines

Number Corner Overheads

Number Corner Student Book Blacklines

Number Corner Calendar Markers

Number Corner Components

Number Corner Manipulatives

The Math Learning Center, PO Box 12929, Salem, Oregon 97309. Tel. 1 800 575–8130.

© 2007 by The Math Learning Center

All rights reserved.

Prepared for publication on Macintosh Desktop Publishing system.

Printed in the United States of America.

QP418, QP544 and QP30   B4TG-GS

P0907 08032

Bridges in Mathematics is a standards-based K–5 curriculum that provides a unique blend of concept development and skills practice in the context of problem solving. It incorporates the Number Corner, a collection of daily skill-building activities for students.

The Math Learning Center is a nonprofit organization serving the education community. Our mission is to inspire and enable individuals to discover and develop their mathematical confidence and ability. We offer innovative and standards-based professional development, curriculum, materials, and resources to support learning and teaching. To find out more, visit us at www.mathlearningcenter.org.

This project was supported, in part, by the National Science Foundation. Opinions expressed are those of the authors and not necessarily those of the Foundation.

ISBN 9781602620070

Acknowledgements

We give special thanks to:

- Donna Burk, for being there from the very beginning.

- Pia Hansen Powell and Susan Rawls, for carrying the torch.

- The late Dr. Michael J. Arcidiacono, for his vision, quiet spirit, sense of balance, and extraordinary teaching skill.

- Dr. Gene Maier, for developing the visual models that have made mathematics more accessible to thousands of children and teachers.

- Debbie Head, Libby Pollett, Mike Arcidiacono, Linda Foreman, and Al Bennett, for developing and writing *Opening Eyes* and *Visual Mathematics*, two resources from which we drew many ideas and much inspiration.

- Martha Ruttle, for her editorial skill, her ability to hold the large picture and the smallest of details simultaneously, her dedication to helping students and their teachers, and her unending search for the truth.

- Tifani Jefferis, for possessing the analytical insight needed to summarize vast quantities of field test feedback, and the compassion, enthusiasm, and teaching experience needed to help us make things better.

- Barbara Blanke for sharing her ideas, knowledge, and Bridges experience with us and with educators across the country.

- Janis Heigl, for sharing her expertise on English-language learners and assessment, and for her sheer love of teaching and learning.

- Becky Boergadine, for her unending support and the many, many contributions she made to *Bridges*, Grade 4.

- Frazer Boergadine, for never allowing us to lose sight of children's ability to make sense of mathematics.

- Gail Lauinger, Kate Ingram, Tracy Longchamp, and Susan Nash, for their expertise and insights about fourth graders and mathematics.

- David Allen, for the integrity and commitment with which he assisted and supported our many field testers.

- Dennis Adams, Nancy Anderson, Becky Boergadine, Frazer Boergadine, Shairlyn Fish, Pia Hansen Powell, Janis Heigl, Sandy Kralovec, Andrea Lane, Trudy Mitchell, Christie Murren, Susan Nash, Cindy Neace, and Joyce Stevens for providing support to fifth grade teachers who implemented the pilot versions of Bridges.

- Raina and Rebecca Deerwater, for their willingness to try out new games and activities as we were developing them.

- Kris Sturdevant, for her role in helping us pull the Grade 4 *Bridges* writing team together.

- The teachers who field-tested *Bridges* units, for permitting us to explore new ideas with their students and taking the time to provide in-depth feedback and suggestions.

We also wish to acknowledge the many children who have been involved with the field-testing of *Bridges*. As always, their enthusiasm, intelligence, and candor have taught us much and have been quite influential in shaping the program.

And finally, we thank our families and friends for their incredible patience, support, and encouragement.

Preface

Chapter 1: Foundations of *Bridges in Mathematics*

Chapter 2: The Structure of the *Bridges* Curriculum

Chapter 3: Content & Planning

Chapter 4: The Teacher in the *Bridges* Classroom

Chapter 5: Classroom & Materials Management

Chapter 6: Assessment & Evaluation

Chapter 7: Supporting Research

Appendix

Preface

....

Getting Started with *Bridges in Mathematics*

The last time you got a new piece of computer software, it undoubtedly came with a users' manual. You probably did one of the following with that manual:

a. Read it carefully from cover to cover before you tried to use the program.
b. Filed the manual away carefully so you could access it later.
c. Tossed the manual aside, installed the software, and began to use it on your own.

If you recognize yourself in b. or c. above, we'd like to convince you that it's well worth your time to read, or at least skim, *Getting Started* before you start teaching *Bridges* for the first time. We also hope you'll put the book in a readily accessible place so you can refer to it throughout the year, even if you're familiar with standards-based teaching and have spent many years in the classroom.

Here are a few features of *Getting Started* that you'll find especially helpful:

- a quick look at the distinguishing features and guiding principles of the program (chapter 1)
- a clear and succinct summary of the program components (chapter 2)
- tips for planning each month, a pacing guide for the year, and some ideas about what to do if you fall behind (chapter 3)
- best practices for increasing student achievement (chapter 4)
- strategies for differentiating instruction and helping English-language learners (chapter 4)
- suggestions for communicating with families (chapter 4)
- tips for setting up your classroom and managing materials (chapter 5)
- a list of the materials provided in the *Bridges* kit and the classroom materials you'll need to supply (chapter 5)
- information about assessment and evaluation (chapter 6)
- an annotated bibliography of related research (chapter 7)
- a list of learning targets (Competencies and Experiences) for Grades 3, 4, and 5 (appendix 1.7–1.12)
- a Math Skills and Concepts Student Report you can use to report student progress through the year (appendix 1.13–1.15)
- suggestions and materials for conducting parent nights, including blacklines to make handouts and overheads (chapter 4 and appendix 1.1–1.6)

We wish you and your students the best as you pursue the mathematical adventures that await you in *Bridges*, and we know things will go more smoothly if you not only read *Getting Started* now, but keep it handy for reference during this school year and the years to come.

CHAPTER 1

Foundations of *Bridges in Mathematics*

A school mathematics curriculum is a strong determinant of what students have an opportunity to learn and what they do learn. In a coherent curriculum, mathematical ideas are linked to and build on one another so that students' understanding and knowledge deepens and their ability to apply mathematics expands. An effective mathematics curriculum focuses on important mathematics—mathematics that will prepare students for continued study and for solving problems in a variety of school, home, and work settings. A well-articulated curriculum challenges students to learn increasingly more sophisticated mathematical ideas as they continue their studies.

NCTM, 2000

About *Bridges in Mathematics*

Bridges in Mathematics is a comprehensive K–5 mathematics curriculum designed to meet the standards established by the National Council of Teachers of Mathematics and many states. Based on years of research on how children learn, *Bridges* was developed by The Math Learning Center with partial support from the National Science Foundation. The curriculum focuses on conceptual understanding and the development of efficient strategies for problem solving. Rather than teach one way to do things, *Bridges* encourages students to develop a variety of problem solving strategies by tapping into their own intelligence strengths (linguistic, mathematical, spatial, kinesthetic, interpersonal). Instruction in a *Bridges* classroom features a blend of whole-group, small-group, and independent activities so that children have opportunities to listen to and learn from everyone in the class.

Bridges facilitates the development of children's mathematical thinking and reasoning abilities by providing age-appropriate problems and investigations in the areas of number, algebraic thinking, geometry, probability, data analysis, and measurement. Some of these problems and investigations grow out of ventures into the everyday world—reading stories, using maps, playing and inventing games, collecting and analyzing data about natural phenomena—while others delve more deeply into the world of mathematics itself. Students are encouraged to explore, develop, test, discuss, and apply ideas; to see mathematics as something that is fluid, vibrant, creative, and relevant.

Distinguishing Features of Bridges in Mathematics

Bridges is based upon the belief that all learners are capable of success in mathematics. The activities and materials in the curriculum are designed to ensure that all students progress toward mathematical fluency, the ability to solve new and challenging mathematical problems with flexibility and confidence. Toward that end, the following features of the *Bridges* curriculum take center stage and distinguish it from other standards-based curricula:

- *Bridges* consistently emphasizes visual thinking across the grade levels.
- *Bridges* integrates concept development and skills practice to promote mathematical fluency.
- *Bridges* spirals through the content strands, revisiting key skills and concepts in a variety of ways at different times over the course of the school year and across grade levels.
- *Bridges* meets the everyday needs of teachers and students from diverse backgrounds.
- *Bridges* improves teachers' mathematical skills and understanding.

Emphasizing Visual Thinking across Grade Levels

Visual thinking is knowledge or understanding that is based on learning through the senses. In math education, this includes using visual representations, physical models, and manipulatives to illuminate mathematical concepts and procedures. Through consistent use of these visual thinking strategies and tools, *Bridges* students build a repertoire of mental models that help them understand concepts, invent problem solving strategies, communicate their thinking, and remember mathematical ideas. Though certainly not the only approach to problem solving, visual thinking enables children of diverse abilities, needs, and strengths to understand mathematical concepts that might otherwise remain abstract and mysterious.

The visual models developed in *Bridges* are accessible to all students regardless of their level of development or stage of language acquisition, making the curriculum language-rich, but not language-dependent. In addition, these visual models become springboards for discussion as students share observations about the models and articulate how their sensory perceptions lead them to mathematical conjectures and insights. In this way, the emphasis on visual thinking facilitates the development of mathematical vocabulary and language skills for all students, including English-language learners.

Visual thinking takes on particular power in *Bridges* because the models extend and grow through the grade levels, providing opportunities for students to connect new learning to past experiences, and to create theories and generalizations based on those experiences. For example, the rectangular array is one of the models used extensively throughout the K–5 curriculum. It is first introduced to kindergartners and first graders as a way to organize collections and think about use of space. In grades 2–5, students use the array as a model for multiplication, allowing them to make generalizations about prime and composite numbers and the various properties of multiplication. The sequence of illustrations and dialog below provides a quick snapshot of this progression.

In kindergarten, children discover that when combined, the paper squares they have each made for a class quilt form a rectangular array. Because it is as tall as it is wide, the array is a square.

Look what happens when we put all our squares together into one big quilt. It's a giant square.

First graders work with rectangular arrays as they determine the best use of paper land squares to set up a model farm. In this context, they consider factors, area, and perimeter.

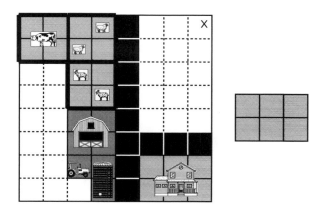

I need to use six squares of land for my horse pasture. There are lots of different ways to put 6 squares together, but it'll be easier to fit everything on my farm if I put my squares together in a rectangle.

When they generate a variety of ways to arrange 12 tile into an array, second graders consider factors and lay the foundation for using the array as a model for multiplication.

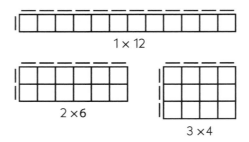

1 × 12

2 × 6

3 × 4

I found 3 different ways to make rectangles out of 12 tile—a 1 × 12, a 2 × 6, and a 3 × 4.

The rectangular array is used in third and fourth grade as a way to explore multiplication and division of whole numbers. In using the array to compute various products, students begin to discover the commutative, distributive, and identity properties of multiplication.

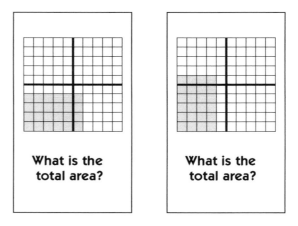

What is the total area?

What is the total area?

Well, I know 6 × 4 is 24, because I can see 5 × 4 and I know that's 20. Then it's just one more row of 4. So 20 + 4 is 24.

It doesn't matter whether it's 6 up and 4 over, or 4 up and 6 over. No matter how you make the array, the product is always 24.

The same model is used in the fourth and fifth grades to explore multiplication and division of 2- and 3-digit numbers.

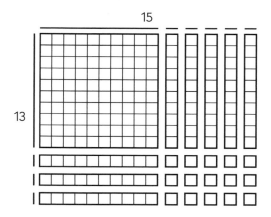

13 × 15? That's a 13-by-15 rectangle. Let's set out the linear pieces first and look at the dimensions. Now we'll fill in the area of the rectangle and see how many units it takes.

It's easy to see the answer. It's 100 plus 50 plus 30 plus 15 equals 195!

There are 13 rows of 15 in this rectangle. That means 195 divided by 15 equals 13 or 195 divided by 13 equals 15.

Fourth and fifth graders also use the rectangular array to multiply and divide fractions in a way that makes these operations accessible to all students.

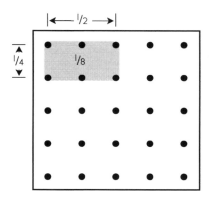

$\frac{1}{4}$ × $\frac{1}{2}$? I can build that on the geoboard. All I need to do is make a rectangle that's $\frac{1}{4}$ by $\frac{1}{2}$. Oh, I see. That little rectangle only takes up $\frac{1}{8}$ of the entire board, so $\frac{1}{4} \times \frac{1}{2} = \frac{1}{8}$.

Visual thinking is not only a way to develop deep understanding of mathematical concepts; it is also an effective problem-solving strategy. In *Bridges*, students frequently use sketches and diagrams to show their thinking and to gain greater insight into the problems they are solving. This is an effective strategy for all learners, challenging those who are comfortable working at a symbolic level to demonstrate their understandings and verify their solutions, while also providing a means of expression for those who are less comfortable working on a purely abstract or symbolic level. All students are encouraged to label their sketches with numbers and operational symbols, and to elaborate in writing about their drawings and diagrams. In this way, visual thinking improves students' mathematical understanding and skills, while also facilitating the development of mathematical vocabulary and communication skills.

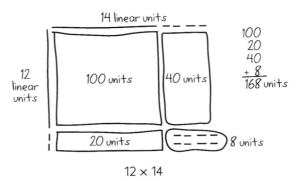

$$12 \times 14$$

The student's computational strategy is based on the sketch, which he or she has made accessible to a teacher or classmate by using clear labels and number sentences to show his or her line of thinking.

Integrating Concept Development and Skills Practice

Developing deep understandings of mathematical processes and developing the skills and computational fluency necessary to function in mathematical situations are sometimes regarded as separate goals, one pursued at the expense of the other. *Bridges*, however, addresses both goals at the same time with continual opportunities to teach and reinforce skills while developing conceptual understanding across every strand, including measurement, data analysis, probability, geometry, and algebraic thinking. Much as phonics skills are best taught in the context of reading whole and meaningful texts, basic mathematical skills are most effectively taught in the context of authentic problems and investigations that facilitate strong conceptual understanding.

In fourth grade, for example, students deepen their understanding of all four operations while developing computational fluency through solving and also posing story problems. As various strategies for solving these problems are shared, the conceptual understanding and computational efficiency of everyone in the learning community grows.

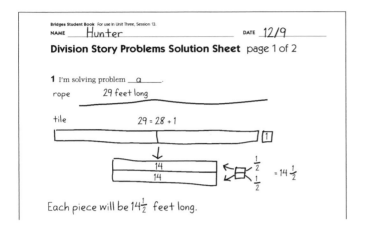

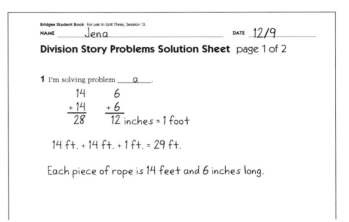

Hunter and Jena used different strategies and modes (pictures for Hunter, numbers for Jena) to solve the problem. In discussing the similarities and differences between their approaches, these two students and their classmates can develop a deeper understanding of the problem, of the operation of division, and of inches and feet.

Although concept and skill development are routinely taught together in the context of problems and investigations, *Bridges* also provides ongoing skill-building opportunities via Number Corner. This collection of daily 15-to-20-minute activities focuses on mastering basic facts, developing computational fluency in the context of story problems, and building such life skills as making change, calculating elapsed time, converting measurements from one unit to another, interpreting graphs and tables, and reading maps. Devoting time explicitly to skills practice ensures that students are equipped with the tools they need to solve problems and explore mathematical concepts deeply during the problems and investigations that comprise the bulk of the curriculum.

The goal of the *Bridges* curriculum is to develop students who are mathematically fluent—confident problem-solvers who understand mathematical concepts and have developed flexible strategies and a solid repertoire of skills. To help students achieve mathematical fluency, *Bridges* provides a unique balance of concept and skill development by teaching them in tandem, using the instructional methods outlined in the diagram on the next page.

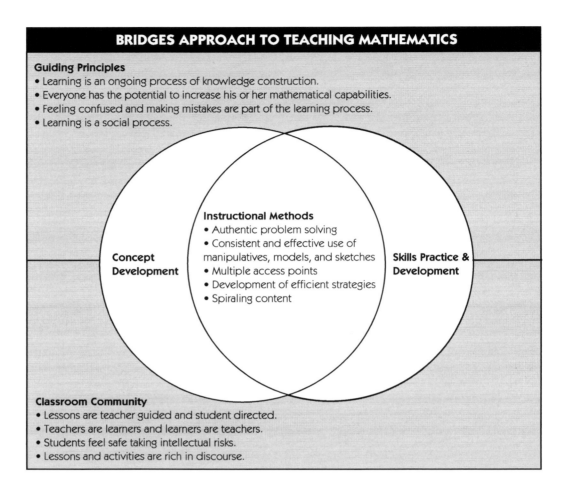

BRIDGES APPROACH TO TEACHING MATHEMATICS

Guiding Principles
- Learning is an ongoing process of knowledge construction.
- Everyone has the potential to increase his or her mathematical capabilities.
- Feeling confused and making mistakes are part of the learning process.
- Learning is a social process.

Concept Development

Instructional Methods
- Authentic problem solving
- Consistent and effective use of manipulatives, models, and sketches
- Multiple access points
- Development of efficient strategies
- Spiraling content

Skills Practice & Development

Classroom Community
- Lessons are teacher guided and student directed.
- Teachers are learners and learners are teachers.
- Students feel safe taking intellectual risks.
- Lessons and activities are rich in discourse.

Addressing Content Strands in a Spiraled Manner

All students will not master skills and concepts at the same time. To ensure that they have multiple opportunities to make sense of mathematical ideas, the *Bridges* curriculum revisits key skills and concepts in different contexts at different times throughout the year and across the grade levels. For example, students who struggle with their multiplication facts at the beginning of fourth grade are given numerous opportunities to develop fluency and finally mastery of these facts in the context of recurring games, activities, and problem-solving situations. Fractions, which are notoriously difficult to teach and learn, are introduced in the early primary grades, explored more formally in third grade, developed extensively this year in Units Three and Six, as well as during numerous Number Corner workouts, and extended even further in fifth grade *Bridges*. This approach provides students many opportunities to master key skills and develop meaningful connections between concepts and skills over an extended period of time, not only within each school year, but from one grade level to the next.

Meeting the Needs of Students and Teachers

As authors, we have stayed in touch with the classroom while writing *Bridges* by talking to colleagues, meeting with focus groups of experienced teachers, and field-testing the lessons ourselves. Over the years, we have dealt with the constraints and pressures, as well as the joys and successes, of teaching. Like other elementary teachers, we have been responsible for children's progress in all areas—language arts, science, health, social studies, music, art, physical education, social and emotional growth, and, of course, mathematics. We have been responsible for assessing students' progress in all areas and reporting to parents throughout the year. We have worked with a wide variety of students, from the gifted to those with greater needs, and held them all dear.

The curriculum has been informed not only by our own experiences, but those of many other teachers. We have collected extensive, detailed feedback from field testers in a variety of settings, from rural schools to urban schools, from schools in which most student receive free or reduced lunch to schools in affluent communities, and from schools with few English-language learners to schools where students speak a wide array of languages. We developed many of the features of *Bridges*—the comprehensive yearlong planning guides, detailed lesson plans, integrated themes, use of technology, assessments, and materials for families—in response to the needs, concerns, and questions of these diverse students and teachers. As a result, *Bridges* is direct, clear, honest, teacher-friendly, and highly responsive to different educational needs and learning styles.

Improving Teachers' Mathematical Skills and Understanding

Because it has been developed by The Math Learning Center, *Bridges* is uniquely attuned to fostering teachers' own mathematical development. Background information is included throughout the curriculum to help teachers understand the big mathematical picture: why each lesson is valuable, what the major mathematical concepts are, and how students will continue to develop these concepts and skills in the future. For many teachers, visual models also provide a new and often surprising way to see, understand, and appreciate mathematics. When teachers are able to see familiar concepts in new ways and develop a sense of the big mathematical picture, their understanding improves, as does their enthusiasm for mathematics, which, in turn, enhances student learning.

The Math Learning Center offers additional opportunities for teachers' mathematical development by providing a variety of workshops, many tailored specifically to the needs of a particular grade level, school, district, or geographical region. Some workshops focus on broad teaching and learning topics, while others focus on a specific resource or curriculum like *Bridges*. All incorporate hands-on activities and classroom discussion and are conducted by highly qualified, experienced teachers who use The Math Learning Center materials and methods in their own classrooms.

We are confident that teachers will find the *Bridges in Mathematics* K–5 curriculum both energizing and effective in meeting the demands of today's classrooms. For more information about The Math Learning Center, including professional development opportunities, call (800) 575–8130 or visit www. mathlearningcenter.org.

CHAPTER 2

The Structure of the *Bridges* Curriculum

Learning mathematics involves accumulating ideas and building successively deeper and more refined understanding. A school mathematics curriculum should provide a road map that helps teachers guide students to increasing levels of sophistication and depths of knowledge.

NCTM 2000

The curriculum is divided into two basic parts: the *Bridges* Units and the Number Corner. There are eight units in Grade 4 *Bridges*. Each unit is composed of between 14 and 22 hour-long sessions that comprise the bulk of your math time. In most sessions, students are engaged in a Problem & Investigation, an activity that focuses on the topic at hand and usually involves whole-group and partner work. Several days during each unit, games that relate to the topic are introduced to the whole class and then revisited by student pairs during Work Places. Work Place days are designed to provide students with opportunities to consolidate and extend their understandings in a different context, and also to provide teachers with time to meet with individuals and small groups in need of extra support or additional challenges. Two or three times a week, students are assigned a Home Connection, which is usually a worksheet but sometimes a game or activity to be completed with a family member.

The Number Corner is comprised of 15- to 20-minute daily workouts that focus on such skills as multiplication and division facts, multi-digit computation, measuring, rounding, calculating elapsed time, building a repertoire of problem-solving strategies, and reading and constructing tables, charts, and graphs. Much of the instruction takes place at the overhead, but a bulletin board display called the Number Corner is central to these workouts. This display features a large calendar pocket chart, a number line, and a collection of record sheets and charts that change from month to month, reflecting the skills and concepts that are being developed. While there are five basic workouts that remain constant over the year, the content of those workouts changes each month to provide students practice with a wide variety of skills. Many teachers use the Number Corner workouts as a warm-up for their daily math time. Others incorporate a Number Corner workout into their morning routine or insert workouts into another time slot during the day.

Both Number Corner and the *Bridges* units contain various forms of assessment so that you can identify students' strengths and needs, make decisions about future instruction based on students' learning, and assign support activities for students who need more practice. These assessments and support activities are covered in greater depth in chapter 6.

The table below shows the unifying instructional techniques used throughout the curriculum and how they correspond to the structure of the Grade Four *Bridges* components.

STRUCTURE OF BRIDGES GRADE FOUR				
Units **Sessions are comprised of**		**Instructional** **Techniques**	**Number Corner** **Months are comprised of**	
Problems & Investigations Activities designed to provide in-depth skill and concept development • Interdisciplinary Learning • Technology Connections • Student Math Journal • Word Resource Cards • Challenge		Whole Group & Small Group Work	**Workouts** Activities designed to foreshadow and review skills and concepts • Calendar Grid • Calendar Collector • Number Line • Computational Fluency • Problem Solving	
Work Places Guided and independent practice at school • Technology Connections • Challenge	**Home Connections** Practice and reinforcement at home • Challenge	Small Group & Independent Work	**Student Book** Guided and independent practice	
Assessment • Observation • Formal and informal interviews • Pre- and Post-Unit Assessments • Work Samples **Looking at Student Work** Student samples and evaluation guidance		Assessment & Evaluation	**Assessment** • Baseline Assessment • Quarterly checkups **Support Activities** Additional practice	

Units

Each unit focuses on a specific mathematical topic, or a few related topics, and is comprised of between 14 and 22 hour-long sessions. A session may contain any combination of three different kinds of activities: Assessments, Problems & Investigations, and Work Places. Each kind of activity is described below in more detail. In addition to the activities, each unit includes Home Connections, assignments given every 2–3 sessions to provide practice with the material being covered in class. The icons and black bar headings in the next few pages will reappear throughout *Bridges*, Volumes 1–4, and are designed to help you navigate through the guides quickly and easily.

PROBLEMS & INVESTIGATIONS

Activities for skill and concept development

Problems & Investigations teach key skills and concepts in the context of problem solving. In each Problem & Investigation, students are usually involved in both whole-group and partner work and are often given time for independent reflection in their student journals or on worksheets related to the session content. Problems & Investigations are the portion of *Bridges* in which most concepts are first introduced.

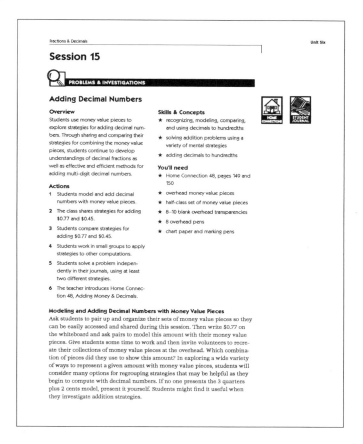

To help students develop the mathematical language needed to communicate their reasoning accurately and precisely, *Bridges* includes Word Resource Cards that show a word along with an illustration of its meaning. A working definition is provided on the back of each card for your reference. These cards can be posted in a classroom pocket chart when the words arise during the course of Problems & Investigations. All of the words can also be found in the Word Resource section of the Student Math Journal.

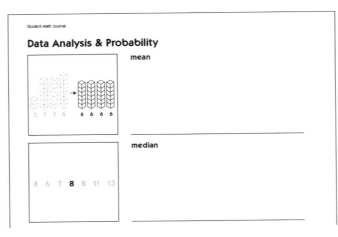

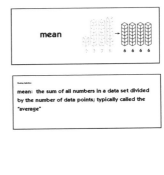

WORK PLACES

Partner games and activities

Work Places are partner games and activities designed to help students consolidate and extend their understandings of the skills and concepts being taught in a particular unit. All but two of the units feature 2 to 4 Work Places, the majority of which are partner games. Each new Work Place is introduced to the whole class in the context of a Problems & Investigations lesson, and students are given time to play the games or do the activities independently a day or two later. While students in the earlier grades do Work Places several times a week or more, in Grade 4 *Bridges*, Work Place days generally occur only one to three times over the course of most units.

Returning *Bridges* students may remember that in previous years their teachers organized the record sheets, game materials, and manipulatives into Work Place baskets for them. This year, the students themselves will be responsible for gathering the materials they need, managing their own record sheets, keeping everything well organized, and maintaining the kinds of behaviors that make these activity periods fun for everyone, including the teacher. Students will have everything they need right at their desks so that they are able to concentrate fully on the games and activities. Because the instructions, game boards, and multiple copies of game record sheets are located in their Work Place Student Books, students are also easily able to return to their favorite games throughout the year as time permits. During the days students are working in pairs on the games and activities, you'll observe and interact with students and help where needed. See chapter 5 for more information about Work Places.

 ASSESSMENT

Diverse methods for assessing skills and understanding

There are a variety of ways to gauge student growth and monitor each student's progress over the course of the year. These include a baseline assessment designed for use sometime during the first week or two of school, pre- and post-assessments that have been built directly into the *Bridges* units, and quarterly checkups of basic skills in the Number Corner. In addition to these formal instruments, some units feature additional assessments in the form of individual interviews, observation ideas, and assignments that have been earmarked as work samples. See chapter 6 for more information about assessments.

Blackline A 2.1 For use in Unit Two, Session 5.
NAME _____ DATE _____

Unit Two Pre-Assessment page 1 of 2

1a ____ Measure and label the length and width of the rectangle below in centimeters.

b ____ Find the area of the rectangle in square centimeters. Show your work.

c The area of the rectangle is _____.

2 Armando is making a friendship bracelet. He bought 11 of each type of bead.

BEAD		COST PER BEAD
⬭	plastic	5¢ each
🛡	metal	10¢ each
●	glass	25¢ each

a ____ Figure out how much Armando spent on beads. Show your work below.

b ____ Write your answer here. Armando spent _____ on beads.

Blackline A 2.2 For use in Unit Two, Session 5.
NAME _____ DATE _____

Unit Two Pre-Assessment page 2 of 2

3a ____ Sketch and label a rectangular array to show 4 × 16.

b ____ Find the answer to 4 × 16 using your sketch. Be sure to show your thinking.

c 4 × 16 = _____

4 ____ Choose one of these multiplication problems.

20	14	30	100
× 6	× 10	× 8	× 16

a ____ Find the answer to the problem you chose. Show your work below using labeled sketches, numbers, and/or words.

b ____ Write your answer here: _____

LOOKING AT STUDENT WORK

Guidance for evaluating student work

After each of the unit pre- and post-assessments, and many of the other assessment pieces including work samples, you'll find a section entitled "Looking at Student Work." These sections feature tips about what to look for in students' responses, and often include samples of student work. In the section that follows each unit post-assessment, you'll find a scoring guide that will help you ascertain whether students are working above, at, toward, or below grade level with regard to the material covered in that particular unit. The scoring guides include annotated examples of student work from each level of proficiency according to our expectations at that time of year.

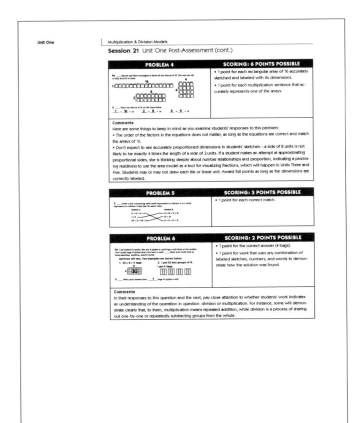

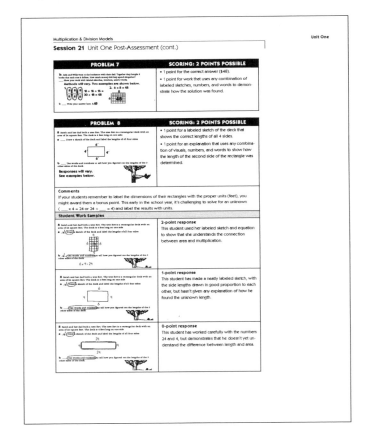

 ANSWER KEY

Answers to All Problems on Student Sheets, Homework, and Pre-Assessments

You'll find answer keys for Bridges Student Book pages and Home Connections at the end of each *Bridges* unit. In addition, keys have been provided for unit pre-assessments and individual interviews. (Solutions and samples of students responses to problems on the unit post-assessments can be found in the relevant sessions themselves.) The keys include answers and, in some cases, examples of strategies fourth graders may use to solve the problems. We have included these for your reference, with the caveat that many of the problems posed throughout the *Bridges* curriculum are open-ended, meaning that although there is usually only one correct answer, there are many ways to obtain that answer.

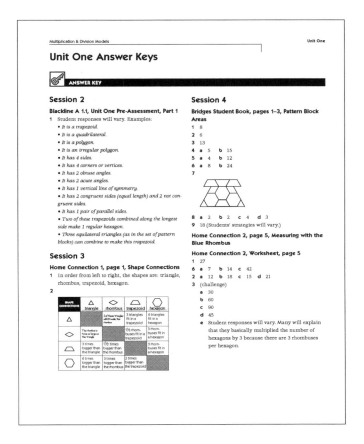

 SUPPORT ACTIVITIES

Games and activities provided for additional support

After many assessments, we provide a list of Support Activities students can use for extended practice. Most are games that can be played in pairs or small groups so students have someone to talk to about their thinking. You'll find these Support Activities in a separate section of the Number Corner Blacklines.

CHALLENGE

Tips for challenging students individually and in small groups

For some Problems & Investigations sessions, most Work Places, and some Home Connections and Bridges Student Book pages, you'll find recommendations for how to increase the challenge level for those students who are already working comfortably with a particular skill or concept. Look for this icon for suggestions, realizing that students may also make their own adaptations to challenge themselves.

HOME CONNECTIONS

Games, activities, and worksheets for practice and reinforcement at home

Homework assignments called Home Connections are included after every 2 or 3 sessions in most units to provide another source of practice and reinforcement. Most Home Connections include a worksheet or two that students complete on their own and return to school; some involve games or activities for students to complete with a family member. Home Connections are intended to support and extend the work students are doing at school, while helping parents and other family members become active participants in their children's math education.

Home Connections For use after Unit Seven, Session 11.

NAME _____ DATE _____

Home Connection 53 ★ Worksheet

Temperature Graphs

1 Below is a graph of the temperatures during a school day at Manuel's school near Miami, Florida.

Manuel's Temperatures

(line graph: Degrees Fahrenheit vs. Time, 9 a.m. 10 a.m. 11 a.m. noon 1 p.m. 2 p.m.)

b Between which 2 hours was there the greatest change in temperature? Show your thinking below.

a Fill out the temperature for each time on the chart below.

Time	Temperature
9 a.m.	74° F
10 a.m.	
11 a.m.	
noon	
1 p.m.	
2 p.m.	

c What do you predict the temperature will be at 3:00 p.m.? Explain your thinking.

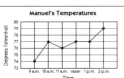

(Continued on back.)

Home Connections

Home Connection 53 Worksheet (cont.)

2 Below is a chart giving the temperatures during a school day at Mina's school near Juneau, Alaska.

Time	Temperature
9 a.m.	11° F
10 a.m.	10° F
11 a.m.	9° F
noon	8° F
1 p.m.	7° F
2 p.m.	8° F

a Plot the temperature for each time on the graph below. Connect the dots to create a line graph.

Mina's Temperatures

(line graph: Degrees Fahrenheit vs. Time, 9 a.m. 10 a.m. 11 a.m. noon 1 p.m. 2 p.m.)

b What do you think the temperature was at 11:30 a.m.? Show your thinking.

c What do you predict the temperature will be at 3:00 p.m.? Explain your thinking.

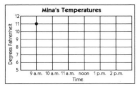

CHALLENGE

3 See if you can collect a single day's worth of hourly temperature data for the place you live. You can use thermometer readings or look up temperatures in a newspaper or on the internet. Create a chart and line graph for the temperatures.

The Number Corner

Every day you'll spend 15 to 20 minutes completing one of the Number Corner workouts. Many of the workouts are whole-group activities, although students are given many opportunities for independent practice in their Number Corner Student Books as well. There are five basic workouts in the Number Corner: the Calendar Grid, the Calendar Collector, Computational Fluency, Problem Solving, and the Number Line. Each workout focuses on a particular skill or concept, often in a problem-solving context, and is carried out using components such as the Calendar Grid pocket chart, the number line, record sheets or charts prepared by the teacher, or overhead transparencies. One baseline assessment and four quarterly checkups have also been included for your use, along with Support Activities that can be used to help students who need additional work with specific skills and concepts. We've provided more information about each of these elements below. The icons and black bar headings in the next few pages will appear throughout the *Number Corner Teachers Guide* to help you navigate through the text quickly and easily.

 CALENDAR GRID

Patterns that develop algebraic reasoning

Students add a marker to the Calendar Grid pocket chart each day, gradually assembling a complete monthly calendar that is related to a particular concept or skill. Updated daily, the Calendar Grid is the focus of whole-class discussion and related activities once or twice a week. Each formal discussion or workout gives students time to make predictions and generalizations about the markers as the pattern emerges over the course of the month. For example, in the month of November, a single triangle appears in a different location on the marker each day, going through a patterned and predictable series of motions every 4 days—slide, slide, turn, flip (i.e., translation, translation, rotation, reflection). This pattern provides ongoing opportunities to develop the language and concepts of motion geometry and serves to introduce ideas that will be explored in more depth later in the year.

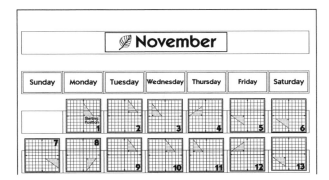

CALENDAR COLLECTOR

Collections that promote deep understandings of measurement and data

Each month, the class collects a unit of measure or a small set of data each day. In September, for instance, a decimeter strip (10 cm) is posted each day on the calendar display board and students keep a record of the growing length in decimeters, centimeters, and meters. This allows fourth graders to investigate the relationship between 1's (centimeters), 10's (decimeters), and 100's (meters) and to practice multiplying and dividing by 10's as they calculate how many centimeters and meters they have in their growing collection of decimeters. Updated daily, the Calendar Collector is a focus of whole-group discussion and related activities once or twice a week.

Decimeters Record Sheet			
Day	Meters	Decimeters	Centimeters
1	$\frac{1}{10}$ m	1 dm	10 cm
2	$\frac{2}{10}$ m	2 dm	20 cm
3	$\frac{3}{10}$ m	3 dm	30 cm
4	$\frac{4}{10}$ m	4 dm	40 cm
5	$\frac{5}{10}$ m	5 dm	50 cm
6	$\frac{6}{10}$ m	6 dm	60 cm
7	$\frac{7}{10}$ m	7 dm	70 cm
8	$\frac{8}{10}$ m	8 dm	80 cm
9	$\frac{9}{10}$ m	9 dm	90 cm
10	1 m	10 dm	100 cm
11	$1\frac{1}{10}$ m	11 dm	110 cm
12	$1\frac{2}{10}$ m	12 dm	120 cm
13	$1\frac{3}{10}$ m	13 dm	130 cm
14	$1\frac{4}{10}$ m	14 dm	140 cm
15	$1\frac{5}{10}$ m	15 dm	150 cm

COMPUTATIONAL FLUENCY

Activities and games designed to improve computational fluency

The purpose of this workout is to provide review and practice with multiplication and division facts throughout the year in the form of worksheets, timed exercises, and games.

PROBLEM SOLVING

Computation in the context of problem solving

Each week, students solve one or two story problems and then share their strategies and solutions with classmates. As the year progresses, students move toward identifying strategies that are particularly effective for certain kinds of problems. Some of these strategies include making a sketch, looking for a pattern, making an organized list, using logical reasoning, guessing and checking, and simplifying the problem in some way.

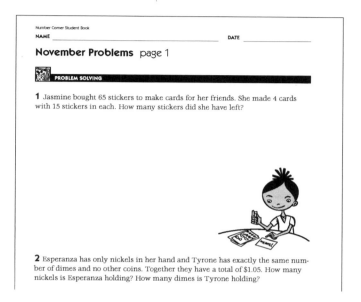

Number Corner Student Book

NAME _____ DATE _____

November Problems page 1

PROBLEM SOLVING

1 Jasmine bought 65 stickers to make cards for her friends. She made 4 cards with 15 stickers in each. How many stickers did she have left?

2 Esperanza has only nickels in her hand and Tyrone has exactly the same number of dimes and no other coins. Together they have a total of $1.05. How many nickels is Esperanza holding? How many dimes is Tyrone holding?

NUMBER LINE

Exploring multiples and place value on a number line

From the first through the hundredth day of school, students enter a number on a large number line posted near the calendar display board to show how many days they have been in school. The numbers on this line serve as a springboard for exploring the multiples of 2 through 9 over the course of many months. In November, an open number line is also introduced at the overhead and used to help students practice rounding whole numbers. By the end of the school year, students will be working with decimals and fractions on the open number line as well.

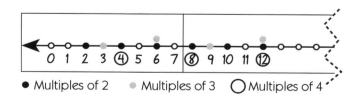

● Multiples of 2   ● Multiples of 3   ○ Multiples of 4

ASSESSMENT

Quarterly checkups of skills

The assessments for the whole year of Number Corner can be found in their own section of the Number Corner Blacklines. The first is a baseline assessment of students' skills with basic addition, subtraction, and multiplication facts, multi-digit computation, place value, probability, and data analysis. You can administer this optional assessment at the beginning of the year to get a sense of students' comfort level with these concepts and skills. If needed, you may also use this baseline assessment as an additional piece of evidence with which to diagnose students' needs and qualify them for special services.

The other assessments are quarterly checkups designed for use at the end of October, January, March, and May to coincide with parent-teacher conferences and grading periods. The checkups are provided to help you examine students' growth in a variety of strands over long periods of time.

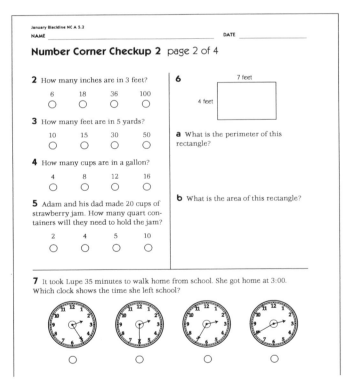

January Blackline NC A 5.1

NAME _____   DATE _____

Number Corner Checkup 2 page 1 of 4

1 Solve these multiplication facts.

2 ×9	5 ×3	7 ×6	3 ×7	4 ×5	6 ×7	8 ×2
3 ×9	6 ×3	5 ×4	4 ×7	9 ×6	8 ×3	7 ×8
9 ×7	7 ×3	4 ×4	6 ×6	5 ×5	0 ×6	1 ×7
4 ×1	9 ×8	3 ×9	8 ×8	5 ×7	10 ×7	7 ×9
10 ×3	2 ×7	4 ×3	4 ×6	5 ×6	6 ×8	7 ×7
0 ×9	4 ×9	4 ×8	5 ×9	5 ×8		

SUPPORT ACTIVITIES

Games and activities provided for additional support

After each checkup, we have recommended a few activities for students who need extra support with particular skills and concepts. All Support Activities are located in a separate section of the Number Corner Blacklines and can be used at your discretion any time of the year. Most are games that can be played in pairs or small groups with adult supervision so students have someone to talk to about their thinking. We recommend making these available for an educational assistant, parent volunteer, or title or resource teacher to use with selected students during a time other than your regular math instruction. Based on their performance on the checkups, you'll be able to determine which students would benefit from a particular Support Activity and can assign them to work with an adult on that activity. You can also send specific activities home with students for extra practice with their families. We'd also encourage you to re-use any Number Corner games that will provide practice with skills and concepts students continue to find challenging.

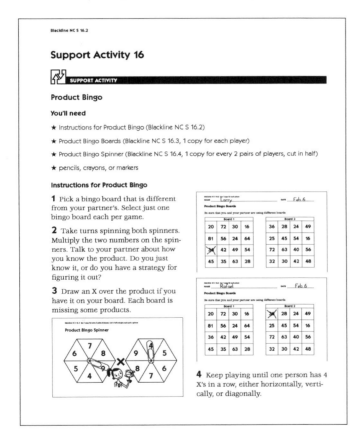

ANSWER KEY

Answers to all student sheets and assessments

You'll find answer keys for the Number Corner Student Book pages, as well as any assessments that may have been included in a given month, at the end of each month's write-up. The keys include answers and, in some cases, examples of strategies fourth graders may use to solve the problems. We have included these for your reference, with the caveat that a fair number of the problems posed in the Number Corner workouts are open-ended, meaning that although there is usually only one correct answer, there are many ways to obtain that answer.

NUMBER CORNER STUDENT BOOK

Worksheets for independent and partner practice

The Number Corner Student Book provides opportunities for independent practice and engaged involvement with the skills and concepts covered in each month's workouts. These pages are integral to the Problem Solving and Computational Fluency Workouts, and take the place of whole-group discussions during the other three workouts with increasing frequency as the year progresses. Many of the items in the Number Corner Student Book are similar to the kinds of questions students will see on standardized tests. However, students are usually prompted to extend their thinking by answering open-ended questions and using sketches, numbers, and words to explain what they know. In this way, these pages do triple duty, giving students independent practice with important skills and concepts, preparing them for the kinds of questions they'll see on norm-referenced or standardized tests, and providing you with deeper information about their problem-solving methods and conceptual understandings.

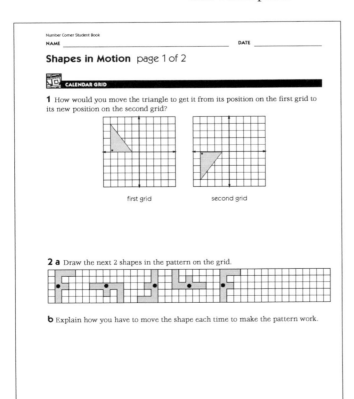

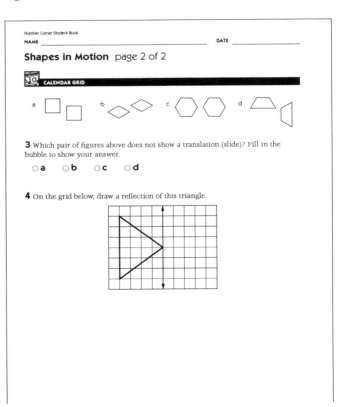

Overview of Program Resources

Getting Started

Provides

Valuable information to introduce teachers to the *Bridges* program and help them use it more effectively and efficiently.

What's Inside

★ An overview of the *Bridges* program

★ Yearlong planning suggestions

★ Yearlong content synopsis

★ Correlation to the NCTM standards

★ Effective teaching practices and classroom management

★ Assessment and evaluation information

★ Annotated bibliography of supporting research

★ Competencies and experiences

★ Materials for family presentations

Number Corner Teachers Guide

Provides

Four or five daily skills workouts for each of the nine months in the school year. Also includes four quarterly skills checkups and one baseline checkup that may be administered at the beginning of the year.

Mathematical Content in Number Corner

★ analyzing and extending patterns

★ developing place value concepts including rounding

★ performing geometric transformations (flips, slides, and turns)

★ figuring elapsed time

★ exploring the concept of functions

★ locating and identifying coordinates on a map

★ measuring length, area, perimeter, and liquid capacity

★ collecting data and interpreting graphs

★ conducting and interpreting probability experiments

★ developing fluency with basic multiplication and division facts

★ performing multi-digit computations in the context of story problems

★ estimating

★ working with money and making change

★ developing problem solving strategies that can be used in many situations

★ understanding fractions and decimals

What's Inside Each Month

★ Introduction to each month

★ Planner for each month

★ Materials list for each month

★ 4 or 5 workouts per month that introduce and reinforce specific skills all year long. Fourth grade workouts include:
  • Calendar Grid
  • Calendar Collector
  • Computational Fluency
  • Problem Solving
  • Number Line

★ Assessment: Quarterly checkups of skills

★ Support Activities: Recommendations for using Support Activities with select students

★ Answer Keys: Answers to all problems on student sheets and assessments

Ancillary Number Corner Materials

Number Corner Overheads
Color and black-and-white overheads used in the Number Corner workouts.

Number Corner Blackline Masters
Blacklines used for Number Corner workouts, assessments, and Support Activities.

Number Corner Student Book Blacklines
Student activity pages for Number Corner workouts, independent practice, and test preparation. (You can purchase consumable Number Corner Student Books individually or in sets of 10 directly from The Math Learning Center.)

Number Corner Calendar Markers
9 sets of color calendar markers.

Number Corner Components
A ready-made wall-size number line.

Number Corner Manipulative Kit and Wall Charts
Contains the Calendar Grid pocket chart and manipulatives for interactive demonstrations and student use. Quantities are based on a class size of 30 students. (See page 94 for a detailed list.)

Bridges in Mathematics Teachers Guides, Volumes One–Four

Provide

All the instructional material needed to conduct the Problems & Investigations, Work Places, assessments, support, and Home Connections for a unit. There is also an introduction for each unit that covers the big mathematical ideas and planning considerations.

What's Inside Volume One

★ Unit 1: Multiplication & Division Models (21 sessions)

★ Unit 2: Place Value & Multiplication with Larger Numbers (21 Sessions)

What's Inside Volume Two

★ Unit 3: Fractions & Division (20 Sessions)

★ Unit 4: Geometry & Measurement (21 Sessions)

What's Inside Volume Three

★ Unit 5: Probability & Data Analysis (18 Sessions)

★ Unit 6: Fractions & Decimals (22 Sessions)

What's Inside Volume Four

★ Unit 7: Algebraic Thinking (14 Sessions)

★ Unit 8: Wingspans: Measurement & Data Analysis (19 Sessions)

What's Inside Each Unit

★ Introduction

★ Planner

★ Materials list

★ 14–22 hour-long sessions. Each session may include any combination of the following elements.

  • Problems & Investigations: Whole group lessons that teach key skills and concepts in the context of problem solving are featured in nearly every session. Word Resource Cards help introduce math vocabulary. The Student Math Journal provides space for recording information, solving problems, reflecting on learning, and making notes about vocabulary.

  • Best Practice Tips: Tips are provided about effective teacher practices that increase student achievement and support English-language learners.

  • Technology Connections: Specific activities require students to use the calculator as a problem solving tool. These activities are marked with a technology icon.

  • 21 Work Places: Work Places are games and activities designed to extend and enhance children's math skills and conceptual understanding through the year. They provide opportunities for choice, collaboration, and cooperation. Work Places involve the use of manipulatives or models.

- Challenge: Challenge suggestions provide learning extensions for use in small group or independent activities.

- Home Connections: Homework assignments serve as another source of practice and reinforcement and help families become active participants in their children's education. Assignments generally include a game or project for students and their families to do together, along with a worksheet.

- Assessment: Multiple forms of assessment are integrated directly into *Bridges*. Forms of student assessment include: informal observation, individual interviews, work samples, and paper/pencil assessments.

- Looking at Student Work: These sections explain what you are likely to see in students' work on assessments and work samples and provide guidance on how to score students' work using a scoring guide that contains student work samples. Tips are provided for offering additional support for struggling students.

- Answer Keys: Answers are provided for all student sheets, homework, and pre-assessments.

Ancillary Bridges Materials

Bridges Overheads
Color and black-and-white overheads used in sessions.

Bridges Blacklines
Blacklines used for sessions and assessments.

Bridges Student Book, Blacklines*
Worksheets for independent and partner use during sessions.

Work Place Student Book Blacklines*
All instructions, record sheets, cards, and gameboards needed for students to complete each Work Place at least twice, as well as a Work Place Log for the whole year.

Word Resource Cards
A quick and useful tool for introducing and reinforcing key math vocabulary for the entire year. Each card contains spelling and pictures of a vocabulary word on the front and a working definition of the term on the back.

Student Math Journal Blacklines*
Space for students to record information, solve problems, reflect on their own learning, and make notes about new vocabulary. Journal pages contain a light grid and writing lines.

* You can purchase consumable Bridges Student Books, Work Place Student Books, and Student Math Journals individually or in sets of 10 directly from The Math Learning Center.

Home Connections Blacklines

Homework assignments that provide another source of practice and reinforcement that encourages families to become active participants in their children's math education. (You can purchase consumable Home Connections books individually or in sets of 10 directly from The Math Learning Center.)

Bridges Manipulative Kit

Contains overhead pieces, along with manipulatives for interactive demonstrations and student use. Quantities are based on a class size of 30 students. (See page 93 for a detailed list.)

Literature

One copy of each of the following:

★ *Spaghetti and Meatballs for All: A Mathematical Story* by Marilyn Burns

★ *Once Upon a Dime: A Math Adventure* by Nancy Kelly Allen

★ *A Remainder of One* by Elinor J. Pinczes

★ *Sea Squares* by Joy Hulme

★ *Birds: Nature's Magnificent Flying Machines* by Caroline Arnold

CHAPTER 3

Content & Planning

Nearly three-quarters of U.S. fourth graders report liking mathematics (Silver, Strutchens, and Zawojewski 1997). They find it practical and believe that what they are learning is important. If the mathematics studied in grades 3–5 is interesting and understandable, the increasingly sophisticated mathematical ideas at this level can maintain students' engagement and enthusiasm. But if their learning becomes a process of simply mimicking and memorizing, they can soon begin to lose interest. Instruction at this level must be active and intellectually stimulating and must help students make sense of mathematics.

NCTM, 2000

Mathematical Themes for Fourth Grade

The National Council of Teacher of Mathematics defines three central mathematical themes for the 3–5 grade band: multiplicative reasoning, equivalence, and computational fluency. All three play a major role in fourth grade.

Multiplicative Reasoning

As students move into the intermediate grades, they need to shift from the additive reasoning they developed during their primary years to multiplicative reasoning. Multiplicative reasoning involves more than the ability to multiply and divide, beginning with the understanding that our base ten number system has a multiplicative structure. For instance, the number 4,275 is really $(4 \times 1000) + (2 \times 100) + (7 \times 10) + (5 \times 1)$ as well as one collection of 4,275 objects. Although it is certainly possible to find the answer to 7×39 by adding 39 seven times (or 7 thirty-nine times), repeated addition becomes increasingly tedious and time-consuming, especially once students move beyond the basics. In fourth grade, students will make the connection between place value and multiplication and develop efficient strategies for multiplying double- and triple-digit numbers by single-digit numbers.

The development of multiplicative reasoning is also required for fourth graders to make progress in strands other than computation. For example, multiplicative reasoning enables students to find the area of 2-dimensional shapes and the volume of 3-dimensional solids efficiently and effectively. Students also employ multiplicative reasoning when searching for generalized patterns that will provide the foundations for proportional reasoning in the middle grades. T-charts, like the one on the record sheet that accompanies the February calendar pattern, are a good way to organize information to show how two variable quantities are related. Well into fourth grade, many students extend this kind of pattern using additive reasoning, figuring out the difference between each number and adding on to create each new element in the sequence. Although this is an accurate way to complete the table or make predictions about upcoming calendar markers, it is not as efficient as using multiplicative reasoning, because when they use multiplicative reasoning, students can determine the output number for any date without computing the intermediary output numbers.

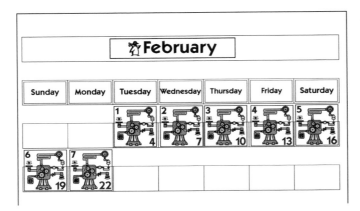

February Calendar Record Sheet		
Input Number	Output Number	Observations & Predictions
1	4	Maybe it'll add 3 each time.
2	7	Now it added 5, not 3.
3	10	It added 7 this time.
4	13	Every new number on the Out side is 3 more than the one before.
5	16	Tomorrow it will be 10, and the day after, it will be 22. It's always 3 more.
6	19	It goes up by 1 on the In number and by 3 on the Out number.
7	22	The Out number is way more than double the In number. It's more like 3 times the In number.

Keith *What will the output number be on the 10th? Well, let's see. The pattern is adding 3 each day, so 22 + 3 = 25, and 25 + 3 = 28, that's the 9th. And 28 + 3 = 31, so the output number on the 10th will be 31.* (additive reasoning)

Maria *I think the output number on the 10th will be 31 because each day, the output number is 3 times the date plus 1. Look at the 4th. The output number is 3 × 4 + 1. And on the 7th, it's 3 × 7 + 1. It works that way every day.* (multiplicative reasoning)

Equivalence

Students' ability to recognize, create, and use equivalent representations of numbers and geometric objects should also increase in fourth grade. Examining equivalence helps students develop efficient strategies for computing and solving problems. For example, students who can see 24 as 20 + 4, 25 – 1, and 2 × 12 have several different options for calculating 7 × 24, all of which are at least as efficient as the traditional algorithm for double- by single-digit multiplication.

Students *7 × 24? That's easy. It's just (7 × 20) + (7 × 4). That's 140 + 28 = 168.*
I thought of it like 7 quarters. I know that 7 quarters is $1.75, but I have to subtract off 1 group of 7 because we're only doing 7 × 24. So it's 168. Here's another way. 24 is twice 12, and I know that 7 × 12 = 84. So twice 84 is 168.

As fourth graders develop fraction and decimal sense, equivalence plays a vital role in helping them understand the connection between the common fractions and decimals. For example, given a wide variety of experiences, students will come to think of $1/2$ in many ways, including half an hour, or 30 minutes out of 60; half an inch; a 2-out-of-4 or 50-50 chance to pull a red tile out of a bag that contains 2 red and 2 green tile; or half a dollar, which is 0.50.

Computational Fluency

Computational fluency refers to having efficient, accurate, and generalized methods for computing that are based on well-understood properties and number relationships. When students' computational fluency is based on a solid grasp of number properties and relationships, they view algorithms as tools for solving problems rather than the goal of mathematics study. Students who are computationally fluent perform calculations mentally or use paper-and-pencil sketches, numbers, or algorithms depending on the problem. Computational fluency is enhanced by students' use of estimation strategies to judge the reasonableness of their solutions.

In fourth grade, the emphasis is on computational fluency with multiplication facts to 12×12. *Bridges* uses the four-pronged approach described below to help develop students' fluency with those multiplication facts.

1. First, you'll provide conceptual instruction that focuses on strategies, an understanding of the operation of multiplication, and the patterns among the facts. This instruction occurs in Unit One and in the September–December Computational Fluency Workouts, as well as many Problem Solving Workouts.

2. The conceptual instruction is followed by opportunities to practice strategies and build speed and fluency with the facts. This practice most often takes the form of games and is also included in the September–December Computational Fluency Workouts.

3. Third, you'll assess students to guide further instruction, using un-graded timed checkups called Quick Facts in the Number Corner Computational Fluency Workouts, as well as more conceptually oriented and problem-solving-related assessments in the units and Number Corner. While we do not advocate timed drill, it is only through timed checkups that teachers can assess whether students have the speed that is an essential component of computational fluency.

4. Finally, you'll support students in their areas of need with further instruction and practice informed by the assessments. Guidance is provided about which Support Activities to use with students who need further practice with specific groups of multiplication facts.

Mathematical Themes Across the Content Strands

All three themes—multiplicative reasoning, equivalence, and computational fluency—increase in complexity throughout the 3–5 grade band and reappear in each of the five content strands: number and operations, algebraic thinking, geometry, measurement, and data analysis and probability. Your students will have an opportunity to construct an understanding of the following concepts and skills in the five content strands through a variety of models and experiences. The descriptions below are meant as a guide: not all of your students will master each and every concept and skill by the end of the year, and your state standards and benchmarks will provide more specific guidance about your community's expectations for fourth graders' mathematical learning.

Computation & Number

By the end of fourth grade, most children will have a very firm understanding of addition, subtraction, multiplication, and division, as well as a grasp of the relationships between the four operations. They will have mastered their multiplication facts and developed efficient strategies for quickly determining their division facts. They will be efficient and accurate at multiplying 2- and 3-digit numbers by 1-digit numbers, and well on their way to understanding the process of division beyond the basics as well. By the end of the year, fourth graders will have worked fairly extensively with fractions and decimals to hundredths and be able to read, interpret, and model both using various concrete models, including money. They will have explored addition and subtraction of both fractions and decimals, and come to understand some of the connections between the two kinds of numbers.

Algebraic Thinking

By the end of the year, fourth graders will be able to describe, extend, and make conjectures and generalizations about numeric and geometric patterns. They will extend number patterns that involve adding or multiplying a single-digit number such as 3, 6, 9, 12 (add 3 to generate each new number) or 2, 6, 18, 54 (multiply by 3 to generate each new number), and will also begin to work with sequences such as the triangular (1, 3, 6, 10, 15) and square numbers (1, 4, 9, 16, 25). Given a specific rule, they will create or complete a table of values; given a table of values, they will generate the rule to explain how each number relates to its partner. Students will use patterns to make predictions and solve problems; translate situations into tables, charts, and graphs, as well as numerical expressions and equations; and start to explore variables.

Geometry

Although fourth graders are still inclined to describe and compare 2- and 3-dimensional shapes in terms of their attributes and properties, they will begin to make informal deductions about shapes as well. When looking at a rectangle, most second graders will be able to explain that it has 4 corners, 4 straight sides, and 2 pairs of equal sides. Some third graders and many fourth graders might say that the rectangle is a quadrilateral with 2 sets of parallel sides and 4 right angles (90 degrees each). With guidance and support, some fourth graders will be moving in the direction of being able to say that a square is a rectangle because it has 4 right angles and the definition of a rectangle is a quadrilateral with 4 right angles. By the end of fourth grade, students will have had enough spatial experiences to combine and subdivide 2- and 3-dimensional shapes with confidence, predict and describe or show the results of transformations (flips, slides, and turns), and understand the connection between transformations and congruence. They will also be able to locate and identify coordinates on grids, maps, and other charts.

Measurement

Fourth graders will select the most appropriate tool and unit (U.S. customary or metric) to measure length, weight or mass, capacity (volume), and time. They will make reasonable estimates for the object being measured and carry out basic conversions between familiar units. They will also be able to find the area and perimeter of rectangles, and will have had experiences finding the surface area and volume of rectangular solids.

Data Analysis & Probability

Fourth graders will read and interpret a wide variety of graphs, including line plots, scatter plots, pictographs, and bar, line, and pie or circle graphs. They will draw conclusions and make predictions based on these graphic displays. They will find the mode (most common value), range, median, and mean of a data set. By the end of the year, fourth graders will be able to collect data and present it on a graph, choosing an appropriate scale and labeling the graph accurately. Fourth graders are also expected to move beyond the magical beliefs about probability held by younger students toward the understanding that likely and unlikely outcomes depend on initial conditions, at least in the long run. Students should be able to list the possible outcomes of a given situation such as flipping a coin, rolling a die, or spinning a spinner, and state the probability of a particular outcome in numerical terms. They should also begin to understand the effect of sample size.

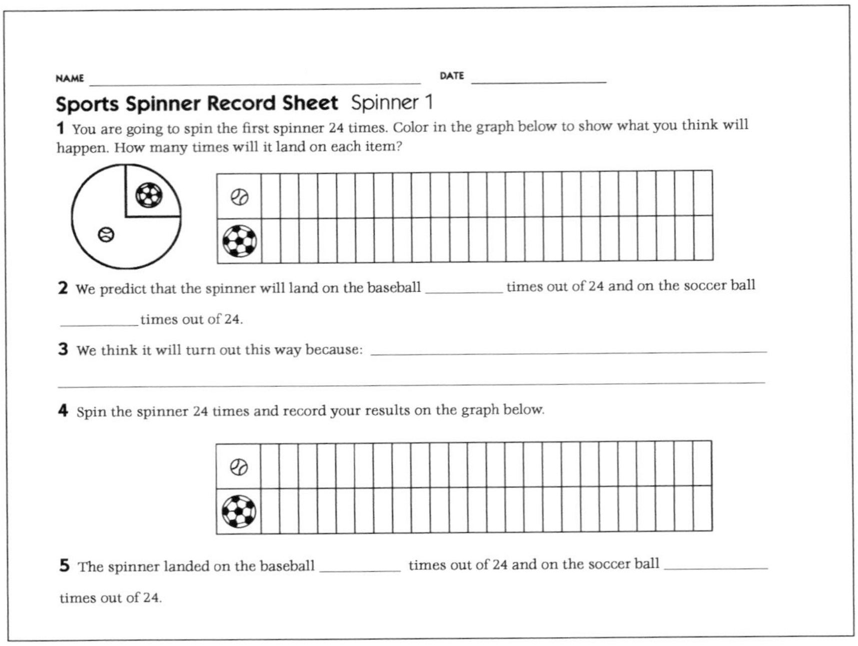

NAME _____ DATE _____

Sports Spinner Record Sheet Spinner 1

1 You are going to spin the first spinner 24 times. Color in the graph below to show what you think will happen. How many times will it land on each item?

2 We predict that the spinner will land on the baseball _____ times out of 24 and on the soccer ball

_____ times out of 24.

3 We think it will turn out this way because: _____

_____

4 Spin the spinner 24 times and record your results on the graph below.

5 The spinner landed on the baseball _____ times out of 24 and on the soccer ball _____

times out of 24.

First Grader *That soccer ball is bigger than the baseball so it will win.*

Second Grader *The baseball won a lot of times so far, so I think it will win now.*

Third Grader *The soccer ball only takes up a fourth of the spinner. The baseball is three-fourths. I think the baseball will win because it has a better chance.*

Fourth Grader *You have a 3 out of 4 chance of spinning a baseball, but you can get either the baseball or the soccer ball for any spin. If you make 400 spins, though, somewhere around 300 of them will probably come out on the baseball.*

Correlation to NCTM Standards

The chart on the next page shows how the expectations for fourth graders' mathematical learning, based on the NCTM standards, are met throughout the year in Grade 4 *Bridges*. You'll notice that the process standards are an integral part of the *Bridges* curriculum. See appendix 1.3 for more information about the five process standards.

CORRELATIONS TO NCTM STANDARDS

	Content Standards					Process Standards				
▽ 1–2 Lessons ◇ 3–4 Lessons ○ 5–9 Lessons □ 10+ Lessons	NUMBER & OPERATIONS	ALGEBRA	GEOMETRY	MEASUREMENT	DATA ANALYSIS & PROBABILITY	PROBLEM SOLVING	REASONING & PROOF	COMMUNICATION	CONNECTIONS	REPRESENTATION
Units										
Unit One Multiplication & Division Models	□	◇	○	□		□	□	□	◇	□
Unit Two Place Value & Multiplication with Larger Numbers	□	◇	▽	□	○	□	□	□	○	□
Unit Three Fractions & Division	□		▽	□		□	□	□	○	□
Unit Four Geometry & Measurement	▽	○	□	□		□	□	□	◇	□
Unit Five Probability & Data Analysis	○		▽	▽	□	□	□	□	◇	□
Unit Six Fractions & Decimals	□			▽		□	□	□	○	□
Unit Seven Algebraic Thinking	▽	□	○		□	□	□	□	◇	□
Unit Eight Wingspans: Measurement & Data Analysis	□	◇	◇	□	□	□	□	□	□	□
Number Corner										
August & September	○	□		▽		◇	▽	○	◇	◇
October	○	◇		◇		◇	◇	○	◇	◇
November	○	◇	▽	◇		◇	◇	○	▽	▽
December	○	▽		▽		◇	◇	○	▽	▽
January	◇	▽		◇	▽	◇	◇	○	▽	◇
February	◇	◇			▽	◇	◇	○	▽	▽
March	◇	◇		▽	▽	◇	◇	○	◇	◇
April	◇	◇	▽	▽		◇	◇	○	▽	▽
May & June	◇	▽	▽	▽	▽	◇	◇	○	◇	◇

An Overview of the Mathematics in Fourth Grade *Bridges*

In order to help students reach the mathematical goals laid out in this chapter by the end of fourth grade, *Bridges* offers a clearly articulated program that begins in kindergarten, continues through first, second, and third grades, and moves into fourth with common models, teaching strategies, and objectives. The major mathematical concepts are covered in seven units, while an eighth thematic unit called Wingspans provides an opportunity for students to extend and refine their understandings of measurement and data analysis in the context of a scientific investigation of birds. Each unit introduction includes a chart showing the major skills addressed in the unit. The chart also specifies whether those skills are introduced, developed, or taught for mastery within that unit, as well as information about the other units and months of Number Corner in which those skills are addressed.

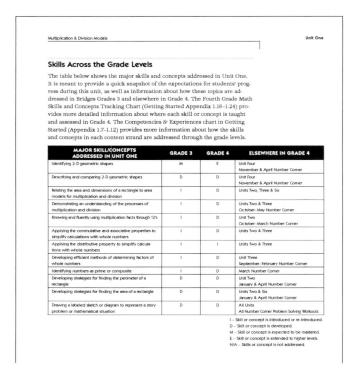

While the units are organized by theme or concept, the Number Corner workouts change each month. Each month's workouts are carefully designed to complement the work students are doing in the units, providing both a preview and a review of important skills and concepts that need to be developed over a long period of time. For example, the Calendar Grid Workout in October features a base four counting pattern that foreshadows the place value work students will do in Unit Two, while the March Calendar Grid pattern revisits the work students did with fractions in Unit Three to help extend their understandings of equivalent fractions. The Number Line and Calendar Collector Workouts in the winter and spring offer instruction in rounding, fractions, and decimals, topics addressed in Units Three and Five that take more time and experience to develop than can be offered in one or two units.

The Computational Fluency and Problem Solving Workouts offer enough consistent practice with the basic multiplication and division facts, as well as multi-digit computation, to make it possible for teachers to delve into lengthy units on geometry, probability, and algebraic thinking without worrying that some of their students will lose their computational skills in the process. The Problem Solving Workout offers students the opportunity to generate and use a number of specific problem solving strategies that are certainly touched upon in some of the units but not made quite as explicit. The lessons in both the *Bridges* units and Number Corner are essential and together help students and teachers meet the expectations for fourth grade mathematics described on the previous pages. The chart below provides a brief summary of mathematical content through the year in both the *Bridges* Units and Number Corner.

BRIEF OVERVIEW OF YEARLONG CONTENT	
Units	**Number Corner Workouts**
Teachers Guide, Volume One Unit One: Multiplication & Division Models Unit Two: Place Value & Multiplication with Larger Numbers **Teachers Guide, Volume Two** Unit Three: Fractions & Division Unit Four: Geometry & Measurement **Teachers Guide, Volume Three** Unit Five: Probability & Data Analysis Unit Six: Fractions & Decimals **Teachers Guide, Volume Four** Unit Seven: Algebraic Thinking Unit Eight: Wingspans: Measurement & Data Analysis	• analyzing and extending patterns • developing place value concepts including rounding • performing geometric transformations (flips, slides, and turns) • figuring elapsed time • exploring the concept of functions • locating and identifying coordinates on a map • measuring length, area, perimeter and liquid capcatiy • collecting data and interpreting graphs • conducting and interpreting probability experiments • developing fluency with basic multiplication and division facts • performing multi-digit computations in the context of story problems • estimating • working with money and making change • developing problem solving strategies that can be used in many situations • understanding fractions and decimals

The Grade 4 Yearlong Content Synopsis Chart on the following pages provide a far more detailed synopsis of the mathematical content of all eight units, including the Problems & Investigations, Work Places, assessments, and Home Connections. In addition, the chart gives a brief synopsis of the mathematical topics covered in the months of Number Corner—including the workouts, assessments, and Support Activities—that correspond to each unit.

GRADE 4 YEARLONG CONTENT SYNOPSIS

UNIT ONE / 21 SESSIONS	AUGUST & SEPTEMBER NUMBER CORNER
Unit One: Multiplication & Division Models	**August & September Workouts**

Unit One: Multiplication & Division Models

Problems & Investigations
- describing and comparing 2-D shapes
- area and perimeter
- developing the area model for multiplication and division
- multiplication and division story problems
- reviewing and developing strategies for learning basic multiplication facts
- prime, composite, and square numbers

Work Places

1A Arrays to 100
developing fluency with basic multiplication facts; applying the commutative, associative, and distributive properties

1B Spinning Around Multiplication
strategies for basic multiplication facts

Assessments
Unit One Pre-Assessment, part 1 (Session 2)
Unit One Pre-Assessment, part 2 (Session 7)
Unit One Post-Assessment (Session 21)
Individual Interview (Session 7)
Work Samples: Sessions 4, 8, 10

Home Connections

1 Shape Connections
describing and comparing 2-D shapes

2 Measuring with the Blue Rhombus
area and multiplication

3 Tetragrams & Pattern Block Areas
spatial problem solving, area, and multiplication

4 Models for Multiplication
posing multiplication story problems

5 The Rectangular Area Model & Area Conversions
using the area model to solve multiplication problems; multiplication and division

6 Factors of 48
primes, composites, factors

7 Solving Multiplication Facts Book
reviewing and developing efficient strategies to solve basic multiplication facts

8 Multiplying by 8 & 9
developing efficient strategies to multiply by 8 and 9

9 Multiplication Facts
multiplication fact practice through 10×10

10 Perimeter of 20
area and perimeter

August & September Workouts

Calendar Grid
place value and multiplying by 10 and 11

Calendar Collector
centimeters, decimeters, and meters; fractions

Problem Solving
expanded notation, place value, comparing ancient and modern numeration systems

Number Line
identifying multiples of 2 and 3 and practicing multiplication facts through 6×6

Assessment
Baseline (optional)
basic addition, subtraction, and multiplication facts; adding and subtracting 2- and 3-digit numbers with regrouping; identifying place value of digits in whole numbers; multiplying and dividing 2- and 3-digit numbers; evaluating a situation that involves probability; reading and interpreting a tally chart

Support Activities

1 Spinning Around Subtraction
strategies for basic subtraction facts

2 More or Less Place Value
expanded notation

3 Make 100
2-digit addition

4 Race to 100 & Back
2-digit addition and subtraction

5 Count Down 400
2- and 3-digit subtraction

6 More or Less Addition
multi-digit addition

7 More or Less Subtraction
multi-digit subtraction

GRADE 4 YEARLONG CONTENT SYNOPSIS

UNIT TWO / 21 SESSIONS	OCTOBER & NOVEMBER NUMBER CORNER
Unit Two: Place Value & Multiplication with Larger Numbers	**October Workouts**

Problems & Investigations • exploring the multiplicative nature of place value in base four and base ten • measuring length and area in metric units • using the area model, as well as landmark numbers, to explore 2-by-1- and 2-by-2-digit multiplication • developing efficient strategies for 2-by-1-digit multiplication • posing and solving story problems for all four operations **Work Places** **2A Moolah on My Mind** money, 2-by-1-digit multiplication **2B More or Less Multiplication** multiplying 1-by-2-digit numbers **2C Optional Challenge: Four 4's** adding, subtacting, multiplying, and dividing **Assessments** Unit Two Pre- and Post-Assessments (Sessions 5 and 21) Work Samples: Sessions 14, 19 **Home Connections** **11 Explore Fours** cups, quarts, and gallons; multiplication facts **12 Measuring in Centimeters** estimating and measuring length in metric units **13 Multiplying by Ten** practicing strategies for multiplying by 10 **14 Spin & Multiply** using the area model to multiply 2-by-1-digit numbers **15 Coins & Arrays** 2-by-1-digit multiplication **16 Design a Floor Pattern** 2-by-1-digit multiplication **17 Which Operation?** representing story problems with equations **18 Moolah on My Mind** money, 2-by-1-digit multiplication	**Calendar Grid** understanding regrouping in the context of base four **Calendar Collector** cups, quarts, and gallons; fractions **Computational Fluency** reviewing and developing efficient strategies for multiplying by 2, 3, 4, and 5; exploring related division facts **Problem Solving** multi-digit addition and subtraction story problems **Number Line** identifying multiples of 2, 3, and 4 and practicing multiplication facts through 9×6 **Assessment** Number Corner Checkup 1 basic addition, subtraction, and multiplication facts; adding and subtracting 2- and 3-digit numbers with regrouping; identifying place value of digits in whole numbers; carrying out simple unit conversions in the metric system; selecting the most appropriate unit of measure; counting and computing with money; telling time to the minute; determining elapsed time **Support Activities** **8 Three Turns to Win** addition of money amounts to $5 **9 Finish with Ten Dollars** addition and subtraction of money amounts to $10 **10 An Hour or Bust to the Minute** telling time to the minute **11 Get Me to the Bus on Time** calculating elapsed time
	November Workouts
	Calendar Grid predicting and describing the results of performing flips, slides, and turns **Calendar Collector** inches, feet, and yards; fractions **Computational Fluency** reviewing and developing efficient strategies for multiplying by 6, 8, and 9; exploring related division facts **Problem Solving** multiplication and division story problems **Number Line** identifying multiples of 5 and 6 and rounding to the nearest 10

GRADE 4 YEARLONG CONTENT SYNOPSIS	
UNIT THREE / 20 SESSIONS	**DECEMBER NUMBER CORNER**
Unit Three: Fractions & Division	**December Workouts**

Problems & investigations

- recognizing, modeling, ordering, and comparing fractions
- understanding fractions as equal parts of a unit whole, parts of a set, length, area, and time
- exploring equivalent fractions
- exploring division with and without remainders
- solving division story problems

Work Places

3A Dozens of Eggs
modeling, recognizing, and adding common fractions
3B Fractions of a Foot Scavenger Hunt
estimating and measuring length in inches; using fractions of a foot
3C Colored Tile Fractions
modeling, recognizing, and comparing common fractions; exploring equivalent fractions
3D Remainders Win
division with and without remainders
3E Line 'Em Up!
2-digit by 1-digit division, with and without remainders

Assessment
Unit Three Pre- and Post-Assessments (Sessions 2 and 20)
Work Samples: Sessions 13, 18

Home Connections

19 Doubles & Halves
area, perimeter, multiplication facts
20 Comparing Fractions of a Foot
identifying and comparing common fractions
21 Modeling Egg Carton Fractions
modeling and comparing fractions, exploring equivalent fractions
21 Eggsplorations
comparing fractions, exploring equivalent fractions
23 Clock Fractions
modeling and comparing fractions
24 Fractions in the Kitchen
measuring capacity, exploring fractions as division
25 Fractions of a Foot Scavenger Hunt
estimating and measuring length in inches; using fractions of a foot
26 Remainders Win
dividing up to $144 \div 12$ with and without remainders
27 Fraction Stories
fraction and division story problems

Calendar Grid
describing, extending, and making verbal generalizations about number patterns to make predictions and solve problems
Calendar Collector
money: fractions and decimals
Computational Fluency
reviewing and developing efficient strategies for multiplying by 10, 11, and 12; exploring related division facts
Problem Solving
computational estimation
Number Line
rounding whole numbers to the nearest 10 and the nearest 100

GRADE 4 YEARLONG CONTENT SYNOPSIS

UNIT FOUR / 21 SESSIONS	JANUARY NUMBER CORNER
Unit Four: Geometry & Measurement	**January Workouts**

Problems & Investigations	**Calendar Grid**
• describing and comparing 2- and 3-dimensional shapes	determining elapsed time; converting from minutes to hours and hours
• reflective and rotational symmetry	to days; fractions
• congruence	**Calendar Collector**
• translations—flips, slides, and turns	conducting a probability experiment; constructing, reading, and
• angles	interpreting a bar graph
• area, surface area, and volume measured in metric units	**Computational Fluency**
• coordinate geometry	practicing multiplication facts through 12 × 12
	Problem Solving
Work Places	using estimation and rounding strategies to add, subtract, multiply,
4A Missouri Squares	and divide
coordinate grids, congruent quadrilaterals	**Number Line**
4B Area Bingo	finding multiples of 7; rounding to the nearest 1,000
finding the area of triangles and rectangles	
4C Mosaic Game	**Assessment**
building figures with line and rotational symmetry	Number Corner Checkup 2
4D Many Faces	basic multiplication facts, adding and subtracting 2- and 3-digit
3-dimensional shapes, congruence	numbers with regrouping, multiplying and dividing 2-digit by 1-digit
	numbers, rounding, carrying out simple unit conversions in the U.S.
Assessments	customary system, finding the area and perimeter of a rectangle, deter-
Unit Four Pre- and Post-Assessments (Sessions 3 and 21)	mining elapsed time, recognizing equivalent forms of common fractions
Work Samples: Sessions 5, 7, 8, 16, 18	and decimals to hundredths
Home Connections	**Support Activities**
28 Origami	**12 Spinning Around Multiplication**
modeling and describing 2-D figures	strategies for basic multiplication
29 Clock Making Puzzle	**13 Array Challenge**
identifying right, acute, and obtuse angles; telling time	understanding multiplication; practicing facts through 6 × 6
30 Drawing 2-Dimensional Figures	**14 Multiplication Challenge**
drawing and labeling line segments, angles, polygons, and parallel,	understanding multiplication; practicing facts through 8 × 8
perpendicular, and intersecting lines	**15 Spinning for Arrays**
31 Plotting Points	using arrays to practice multiplication facts through 9 × 6
locating coordinates of points on a grid; identifying lines of symmetry,	**16 Product Bingo**
naming polygons, recognizing congruent shapes, and identifying dif-	multiplication facts practice
ferent kinds of angles	**17 What's Missing? Bingo**
32 3-Dimensional Shapes	multiplication and division facts practice
describing 3-D shapes	
33 Mirror, Mirror	
performing reflections of polygons on a grid	
34 Net Work	
exploring nets for 3-D shapes	
35 Letter Symmetry	
line and rotational symmetry	

GRADE 4 YEARLONG CONTENT SYNOPSIS

UNIT FIVE / 18 SESSIONS	FEBRUARY NUMBER CORNER
Unit Five: Probability & Data Analysis	**February Workouts**

Problems & Investigations

- predicting and representing all possible outcomes in an organized way
- predicting the likelihood of a particular outcome
- expressing outcomes in verbal and numerical form
- collecting, representing, and interpreting data
- reading and interpreting bar, circle, and pictographs
- exploring range, median, and mode

Assessments

Unit Five Pre- and Post-Assessments (Sessions 1 and 18)
Work Samples: Sessions 4, 11, 15, 17

Home Connections

36 Charting the Possibilities
using a chart to show all possible outcomes of a situation
37 Tree Diagrams
using a tree diagram to show all possible outcomes of an experiment
38 Organized Lists
using an organized list to show all possible outcomes of an experiment
39 Spinner Game
keeping track of experimental results and determining probabilities of various outcomes
40 Sports Statistics
interpreting data in a table and creating a pictograph
41 Data Distances
creating a bar graph, identifying mode, median, and range

Calendar Grid
describing, extending, and making verbal generalizations about number patterns to make predictions and solve problems; exploring the concept of functions
Calendar Collector
conducting a probability experiment; constructing, reading, and interpreting a bar graph; using multiplication facts fluently
Computational Fluency
practicing multiplication facts through 12×12
Problem Solving
multiplication and division story problems
Number Line
identifying multiples of 8 and 9

GRADE 4 YEARLONG CONTENT SYNOPSIS

UNIT SIX / 22 SESSIONS	MARCH NUMBER CORNER
Unit Six: Fractions & Decimals	**March Workouts**

Unit Six: Fractions & Decimals	March Workouts
Problems & Investigations • developing fraction and decimal sense • modeling, reading, and understanding fractions and decimals • relating the area model to fractions • adding and subtracting whole numbers and decimals • locating fractions and decimals on a number line	**Calendar Grid** equivalent fractions **Calendar Collector** collecting and graphing data; measuring in milliliters; constructing and reading a line graph **Computational Fluency** division with and without remainders **Problem Solving** using and identifying a variety of problem-solving strategies; reading and interpreting graphs and tables; fractions
Work Places **6A Decimals More or Less** identifying, modeling, and comparing decimal numbers to hundredths **6B Fractions, Decimals, & Dollars** modeling fractions and decimals with money	**Number Line** prime numbers; rounding to the nearest tenth
Assessments Unit Six Pre- and Post-Assessments (Sessions 1 and 22) Work Samples: Sessions 3, 4, 9, 10, 13, 17	**Assessment** Number Corner Checkup 3 basic multiplication and division facts; adding and subtracting 2- and 3-digit numbers with regrouping; multiplying and dividing 2-digit by 1-digit numbers; solving addition, subtraction, and multiplication story problems; selecting an appropriate number to make an equation true; finding the area and perimeter of a rectangle; reading and interpreting a bar graph and a pictograph; predicting the likelihood of an outcome; fractions
Home Connections **42 The Relationship between Multiplication & Division** using the inverse relationship between multiplication and division **43 Fraction Relationships** comparing fractions **44 More about Cups, Quarts & Gallons** cups, quarts, gallons, fractions **45 Fractions & Base Four** fraction situations and story problems **46 Decimals Are Fractions** connecting decimals and fractions **47 Money, Fraction, & Decimal Showdown** comparing fractions and decimals **48 Adding Money and Decimals** using money to model decimals, adding decimals **49 Decimal Problems** adding and subtracting decimals	**Support Activities** **18 More or Less Addition Big Time** adding 3-digit numbers with regrouping **19 More or Less Subtraction Big Time** subtracting 3-digit numbers with regrouping **20 Larger Numbers on a Line** adding and subtracting 3-digit numbers with regrouping **21 Perimeter Showdown** calculating the area and perimeter of rectangles **22 Spin & Multiply** multiplying 1- by 2-digit numbers **23 Remainders Win** dividing up to 144 ÷ 12 with and without remainders **24 Fraction Race** modeling and comparing fractions **25 Fraction Bingo** modeling and comparing fractions

GRADE 4 YEARLONG CONTENT SYNOPSIS

UNIT SEVEN / 14 SESSIONS	APRIL NUMBER CORNER
Unit Seven: Algebraic Thinking	**April Workouts**

Problems & Investigations	**Calendar Grid**
• describing and extending patterns	finding the perimeters of a variety of shapes and understanding the
• making conjectures and generalizations about numeric and	connection between area and perimeter
geometric patterns	**Calendar Collector**
• graphing patterns; line graphs	equivalent fractions, mixed numbers, and adding fractions
• exploring odd, even, square, and triangular numbers	**Computational Fluency**
• functions	division practice
• exploring the concept of a variable	**Problem Solving**
	multiplication and division story problems, area, perimeter, and
Work Places	fractions
7A Odd One Out	**Number Line**
odd and even numbers, logical reasoning	modeling, recognizing, and ordering decimals along a number line;
7B What's My Rule?	adding decimals
creating and extending number patterns	
Assessments	
Unit Seven Pre- and Post-Assessments (Sessions 4 and 14)	
Work Samples: Sessions 1, 3, 7, 11, 13	
Home Connections	
50 Extending Tile Patterns	
describing, extending, and generalizing patterns	
51 Describing Patterns	
describing, extending, and graphing patterns	
52 Squares on a Checkerboard	
using patterns to solve problems, square numbers	
53 Temperature Graphs	
reading, interpreting, and constructing line graphs	
54 Toothpick Patterns & Puzzle	
describing, extending, and generalizing patterns	

GRADE 4 YEARLONG CONTENT SYNOPSIS

UNIT EIGHT / 19 SESSIONS	MAY & JUNE NUMBER CORNER
Unit Eight: Wingspans: Measurement & Data Analysis	**May & June Workouts**

Problems & Investigations
- collecting, representing, and interpreting data
- exploring mean, median, and mode
- creating, reading, and interpreting tables, charts, bar graphs and line plots
- creating and interpreting scatter plots and trend lines
- measuring weight and length in U.S. customary units; making conversions from one unit to another

Assessments
Unit Eight Pre- and Post-Assessments (Sessions 1 and 19)
Work Samples: Sessions 6, 7, 8, 18

Home Connection
55 Wingspans of Jays & Their Cousins
reading and interpreting a table and a line plot; entering information on a line plot
56 Bird Riddles
coordinate graphing
57 More Bird Riddles
coordinate graphing

Calendar Grid
coordinate graphing and map reading skills
Calendar Collector
multi-digit column addition, reading and constructing tables and graphs, estimation
Computational Fluency
adding, subtracting, multiplying, and dividing using mental strategies
Problem Solving
computation story problems with all four operations
Number Line
reading, ordering, and recognizing equivalent forms of common fractions and decimals; locating fractions and decimals to hundredths on a number line

Assessment
Number Corner Checkup 4
basic multiplication and division facts; adding and subtracting 2- and 3-digit numbers with regrouping; multiplying and dividing 2-digit by 1-digit and 2-digit numbers; finding factors and multiples; reading and ordering whole numbers to 60,000; reading and interpreting a bar graph, pictograph, and circle graph; predicting the likelihood of an outcome; fractions and decimals

Support Activities
26 Round & Add Tens
Rounding 2-digit numbers to the nearest ten and adding 2- and 3-digit numbers
27 Round & Add Hundreds
Rounding 3-digit numbers to the nearest hundred and adding 3- and 4-digit numbers
28 Divide 'Em Up
Dividing 2-digit numbers by 1-digit numbers using models
29 Money, Fraction & Decimal Showdown
Comparing common fractions, decimals, and money amounts with models

Planning Your Instruction

Planning Each *Bridges* Unit & Month of Number Corner

Each *Bridges* unit and each month of Number Corner begins with an introduction that summarizes what will happen in that unit or month. These introductions also describe the big mathematical ideas that tie the activities in each month or unit together, explaining how these ideas are connected to students' prior and future mathematics learning and how students might approach these new ideas. We strongly recommend reading the introductions before beginning the lessons. You may also find it helpful to revisit the introductions periodically as your progress through a unit or month of Number Corner workouts.

At the end of each introduction, you'll find a list of materials needed for the entire unit or month. These lists will indicate if you need to collect any special materials or if any unusual advance preparation is required. The write-up for each workout and session also includes a list of the specific materials needed for that session or workout. In this way, we have provided information about all the materials you'll need for each month or unit, as well as what you'll need each day.

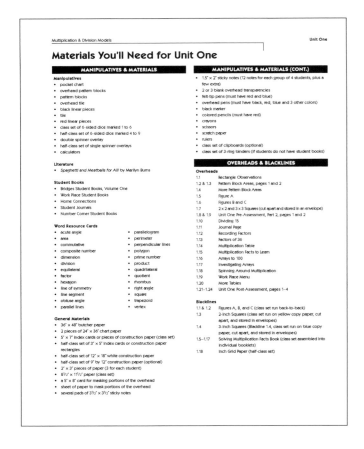

The introductions also include planners. The Unit Planners lay out the entire unit day by day, showing what Problems & Investigations, assessments, Work Places, and Home Connections are scheduled for each day.

Since there are five workouts each month, the Number Corner Planners simply suggest which workout to teach each day of the week and list the skills and concepts involved so that you can make more informed decisions about modifying the plans if necessary. A planner template is included in the Number Corner Blacklines so that you can fill out a day-by-day planner for each month of workouts. We encourage you to be flexible in adapting the combination and frequency of workouts you conduct each month, knowing that some months you may choose to repeat a workout more often than suggested or skip a particular workout altogether based on your students' emerging needs and strengths.

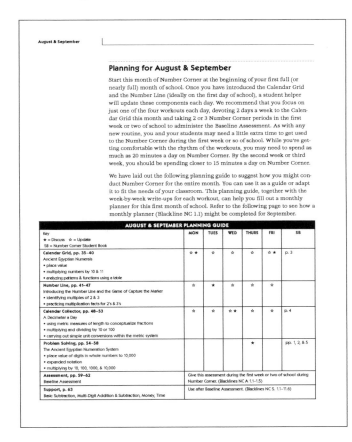

In addition, you'll find two setup pages for each month of Number Corner that provide a visual reminder of what will happen that month. In most cases, you'll post only the Calendar Grid and Calendar Collector, along with their record sheets, as well as the Number Line, on the Number Corner display board.

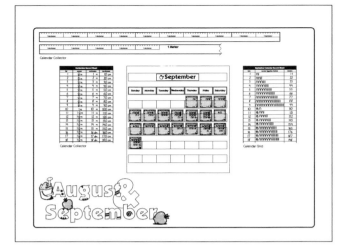

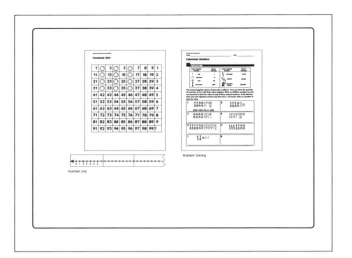

Units vary in length, from 14 sessions (Unit Seven) to 22 sessions (Unit Six). Sessions are designed to last about an hour each, so 20 sessions make up about 4 weeks of instruction if there are no interruptions, assemblies, conferences, or holidays, and if the timing of each session works the same in your classroom as it did in ours. More than likely, these conditions won't hold, and a 20-session unit may take up to 5 weeks instead of 4.

The Number Corner months are more predictable. Because workouts are repeated through the month, you can simply move on to the next set of Number Corner workouts when a new month begins. Although the workouts and sessions dovetail nicely, you can move ahead with Number Corner workouts even if you've fallen a bit behind in a unit.

Allowing for the inevitable interruptions, the fact that some sessions will take 2 days instead of 1, and the likelihood that it will take longer to get through some of the materials the first time you use them, your year might look like this:

YEARLONG PACING		
Month	**Unit**	**Sessions**
August & September	**Unit One** Multiplication & Division Models	21
October	**Unit Two** Place Value & Multiplication with Larger Numbers	21
November		
December	**Unit Three** Fractions & Division	20
January	**Unit Four** Geometry & Measurement	21
February		
March	**Unit Five** Probability & Data Analysis	18
	Unit Six Fractions & Decimals	22
April		
	Unit Seven Algebraic Thinking	14
May		
June	**Unit Eight** Wingspans: Measurement & Data Analysis	19

Planning Each Session

At the beginning of each session write-up, you'll find a brief overview of the session, an actions list, a list of skills and concepts, and a list of materials. Before conducting any session, you'll need to read over the list of materials to make sure you have everything needed to conduct the lesson. We've included a note at the beginning of a session any time advance preparation is needed, for instance, cutting paper to specific dimensions or preparing a chart beforehand. After the overview and lists, you'll find the write-up for the session. The write-up provides detailed instructions about how to conduct the lesson, as well as sample dialog and student work, illustrations, and diagrams. We recommend reading the session all the way through before conducting it for the first time. As you teach the session, the headers, dialog, and visuals provide cues about what to do next. We've also provided space in the margins for you to make notes about each session based on your own experiences.

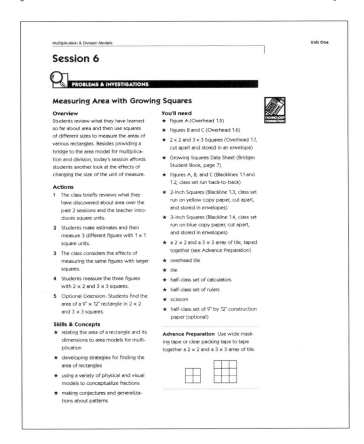

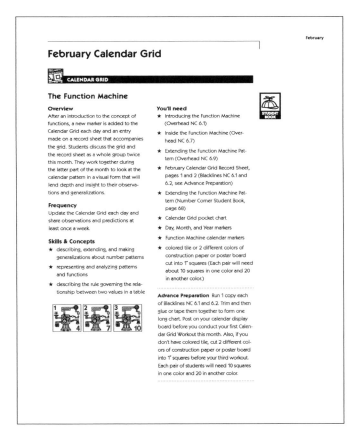

Planning Each Number Corner Workout

The write-up for each Number Corner workout provides an overview or brief summary of that workout, a note about how often to conduct the workout, a list of skills and concepts addressed, and a list of materials you'll need to complete the workout.

Each of these introductory sections is followed by a detailed write-up of how to conduct the workout each week, how to adapt it throughout the month, and how to provide additional support or challenge for those students who need it. You'll see sample dialog, explanatory illustrations, and sample student responses throughout these write-ups. They also include information about pages in the Number Corner Student Book you will use to provide individual practice with the skills and concepts addressed in that workout.

If You Get Behind

It's quite common to get behind in your first year teaching a new program. No matter how comprehensive a program is, you'll need time to adjust to it, and you'll always need to adapt your instruction to respond to the needs and abilities of your own students. When considering your planning and pacing, keep the following points in mind.

1. Much of the instruction in *Bridges* takes place at a problem-solving level. Many of the sessions will be a slight stretch for fourth graders and may not be accessible to all of your students all of the time. While it will be tempting to slow down to make sure every student gets it, we strongly encourage you to keep a fairly brisk pace because the instruction is spiraled. Nearly every concept comes back a second, third, or even fourth time within the year, either in another unit, the Number Corner, or in Home Connections. If students don't get a concept the first time around, they'll encounter that concept again and again in different contexts that provide them new opportunities to make sense of it. We all know from experience that students learn at different rates and in different ways. If you slow down your instruction too much, though, you may deprive students of the very experiences they need to make sense of new mathematical ideas.

2. We have tried to build in allowances for fire drills, assemblies, and days that just don't go as smoothly as you'd like. That's why there are only 156 sessions, even though you probably have a school year that lasts 175 days or more. Many teachers find it helpful to create a few of their own catch-up sessions throughout the year. In about the third week of a unit, for example, you might take half a session to wrap up loose ends from an earlier session or devote some extra time to a particular Number Corner workout, and then give students the second half of the session to return to their favorite Work Places. We find that breaking a catch-up session in half this way keeps students' interest, motivation, and focus high.

3. If taught in conjunction with the Number Corner, the first six *Bridges* units focus on the content most fourth graders will see on district, state, or national assessments. Even if you don't get to the seventh and eighth units your

first year, you will have probably addressed most, if not all, of the content your students will be tested on in fourth grade, as long as you've also taught the corresponding months of Number Corner. The last two units address experiences your students will revisit in fifth grade and serve to deepen and enrich the fourth grade year.

4. You may find that, on occasion, skipping some of the sessions in a unit can help get you back on track. We recommend that you wait until at least your second year teaching the program before removing sessions so that you can make cuts in an informed way, considering the program as a whole, your students' understanding of the concepts, and how various sessions meet your state, district, and school expectations. By your second year, however, you may find that you're more comfortable with the program and that as a result it's easier to stay on track

CHAPTER 4

The Teacher in the *Bridges* Classroom

Teachers establish and nurture an environment conducive to learning mathematics through the decisions they make, the conversations they orchestrate, and the physical setting they create. Teachers' actions are what encourage students to think, question, solve problems, and discuss their ideas, strategies, and solutions.

NCTM, 2000

There are a number of elements that contribute to good educational environments for elementary children, including the people, the curriculum, the materials, and the setup and flow of the classroom itself. None of these works alone, although teachers and their attitudes toward children, learning, and mathematics surely have the biggest impact. In this chapter we discuss the role of the teacher in the *Bridges* classroom and the effective teaching practices *Bridges* has to offer, including strategies for differentiating instruction and for helping English-language learners. Because family members are teachers too, we also offer suggestions about effective ways to communicate with families and engage them in their children's mathematical learning. In chapter 5, we address the classroom management techniques that best facilitate this kind of teaching.

....

The Role of the Teacher in the *Bridges* Classroom

In *Bridges* the teacher's role is that of an educator in the root meaning of the word: one who educes, that is, draws out, the mathematician within every student. The teacher does this by engaging students in activities and experiences that encourage them to explore mathematical concepts in sensory rich settings, report on their findings, and have others accept the validity and value of those findings. The teacher nurtures students' confidence and autonomy in the following ways.

Valuing the process of finding the answer as much as the answer itself
This means listening carefully to students and trying to understand how they get their answers, even when their methods or answers don't make much sense to you. By regularly allowing private think time before group discussions of a problem or idea, you show respect for and interest in student thinking. Providing this time also conveys that you have faith in each student's ideas and trust in everyone's ability to contribute to the discussion—not only those students who are quickest to raise their hands.

When students have regular opportunities to share and debate ideas and reach their own conclusions, they become confident learners who formulate and investigate their own questions, value other points of view, and welcome difficult problems. A focus on student discourse:

- promotes students' reflective thought about their own and others' thinking,
- encourages students to elaborate on their thinking leading to clarification,
- leads to re-conceptualization of ideas and development of new knowledge,
- improves students' self-esteem,
- reinforces the notion that the learner (not the teacher or a text) is the mathematical meaning-maker,
- reveals how a student is constructing knowledge and beliefs, thereby providing ongoing assessment information,
- provides a basis for instructional planning and feedback regarding the effectiveness of instruction,
- and enables the teacher to grow in his or her knowledge about the way students learn and think.

Creating an atmosphere in which it's okay to take risks and make mistakes

If you listen to children with genuine respect and interest, you'll find that they begin to do the same for their classmates. Non-judgmental responses that show acceptance or seek clarification of student views help create an environment in which students feel safe volunteering their ideas and solutions.

When an idea suggested by a student during class discussion is wrong, rather than commenting on its correctness, we generally thank the student for sharing his or her thinking and ask for other volunteers to share their ideas. If a student's reasoning is incorrect and other students don't raise questions or suggest ideas that raise contradictions, we may pose another problem or situation that is likely to do so.

Research suggests that both positive and negative value judgments of student ideas interfere with learning, except when students are learning simple rules or routines. Evaluative responses can come in the form of words, facial expressions, or gestures, and they encourage students to rely on others to gauge the worth of their ideas. In this kind of environment, students' responses tend to reflect what they think the teacher wants to hear rather than what they really think or feel. As a result, we try to keep our responses to student ideas neutral and genuine. That is, we ask questions to follow up on student thinking, to encourage them to extend their ideas, and to get clarification.

Providing time for children to share their strategies with one another

This can take place with partners, in small groups, or in whole-group discussions. For this kind of sharing to be productive, you must establish the habits of listening to and learning from one another as classroom norms. Some teachers find it helpful on the first day of school to have students create a list of behavior expectations for whole-group interaction, which can then be used to help build classroom community throughout the year.

As a general rule, avoid repeating or paraphrasing what students say. Restating what has already been said is usually not a good use of time and, more importantly, takes authority and responsibility away from students. Students quickly realize that they do not have to listen to their peers becuse the teacher will repeat what they say. If there is genuine confusion about what a student has said, invite students to resolve the confusion themselves, by respectfully questioning the student who is sharing or by finding ways to express what that student has said in a different way.

Many sessions include time for students to think-pair-share, that is, think privately, pair up with another student to discuss each other's ideas, and then share ideas together as a class. A variation of this technique suggested in some of the sessions is think-ink-pair-share. This allows students to record some of their ideas using words, numbers, and/or sketches before they start sharing with classmates. Research has shown that these types of cooperative learning strategies increase language opportunities for English-language learners and improve overall student achievement.

Student demonstrations at the overhead or whiteboard are an important part of many *Bridges* sessions, and you'll quickly find that some students are reluctant to share this way at first. You can help them feel more comfortable by inviting them to the overhead with a partner or asking them to transfer their work to a transparency ahead of time to eliminate the pressure of writing and sketching in front of the class. You can offer friendly encouragement to reluctant students by complimenting them privately on their work and asking if they would mind sharing during a class discussion. If they are still reticent, ask permission to share their approach with the class, and suggest that perhaps another time they will feel comfortable demonstrating a strategy.

Displaying student work (assignments, charts, etc.) in the classroom is another way to encourage involvement. While students' work may not be as neat as the displays you create yourself, students of all ages seem to enjoy and pay closer attention to their own and peers' work. This also fosters a feeling of student ownership of the classroom, lets students know that you and others value their work, and reinforces the importance of different views and approaches.

Drawing out mathematical thinking with genuine questions

In order to understand the development of students' mathematical thinking, you will at times observe student interactions without participating, while at other times you'll need to ask questions to learn more about how students are thinking. It is important that such questions are genuine, that is, that they convey real interest in what the student is thinking. If you find that you want to make a point or share information, it is usually best to be direct with the student rather than ask questions to prompt him or her to guess what you are thinking.

Helping children clarify and justify their thinking as they work independently or discuss problems in a group setting

We have included dialogue in many of the lessons to model questioning techniques that may be effective in a specific situation or for a specific topic. We also find that the following key questions are useful in many different situations.

- What do you notice? (about this chart, picture, pattern, problem, etc.)
- What do you see?
- What do you think?

- Do you see any patterns here?
- What might come next?
- What do you predict will happen and why?
- How did you figure it out? (Children who can't verbalize what they did to figure something out can sometimes show it by making a sketch or by using manipulatives at the overhead.)
- Can you draw a picture to show what's going on?
- Does anyone have a different solution?
- Does anyone have a different strategy for solving this problem?
- Can you convince us?
- Can anyone think of a more efficient way?
- How can you be sure that_____?
- How would you describe this problem in your own words?
- Which ones are easy for you? What makes them easy? Let's start with those and see if we can find others that seem easy.

Making decisions about how to proceed with a lesson

One very important role of a *Bridges* teacher is that of decision maker. The text provides a framework to evoke meaningful mathematical discussion and observations related to the session topic. However, each teacher will determine the direction a session takes based on students' strengths, needs, and contributions. The teacher poses a problem, listens to student thinking, and then must make decisions, such as the following:

- I wonder what that student means. What should I do to further elicit her thinking?
- Will pursuing this student's idea be mathematically productive?
- I don't know how/whether this idea works. Am I willing to take a risk and explore it with the class?
- Will following this student's idea lose other students?
- Shall I sacrifice overall student interest for a brief period in order to build confidence in this student who wants to share and rarely volunteers?
- The idea that came up isn't related to the big mathematical idea of this session. Should we pursue it now or come back to it later?
- Do I need to pose a different twist on this problem in order to find out how students are thinking?
- Am I focusing too much on mastery or do students truly need more time?
- I wanted this idea to come up here and it didn't. How critical is it to the main ideas of this session? Will it come up later? Will sharing my ideas now move things along or block student thinking?

Understanding that children won't always get it, even when you explain things several times and try to help them along

This is especially true when you pose a problem to your entire group at once. There are times when you can scale the problem down to meet an individual's needs, but there are also times when you have to let go. This is one of the reasons we have included Work Places in all but Units Five and Eight. These games and activities often provide a return to skills and concepts introduced during the Problems & Investigations and allow you to work more easily with individuals or small groups. Skills and concepts also resurface regularly in the Number Corner, the Home Connections, and the units themselves.

Teaching *Bridges* effectively requires a shift away from teaching by telling and a move toward believing that students need to construct their own understandings in order to learn mathematics, and that they are capable of doing so. Such a shift is not easy, as we know from our own teaching experiences. Teaching via problem solving requires accepting the fact that students won't always get it, that there will be frustration and discomfort sometimes, and that sometimes children will walk away from lessons puzzled and confused. However, each lesson is designed in such a way that every child has some access to each problem posed and something to gain from working the problem.

Effective Teacher Practices within *Bridges*

Thirty-five years of research provide remarkably clear guidance regarding the steps schools can take to improve student achievement. Classroom teachers are influenced by state, district, and school decisions and policies, yet researchers agree that the decisions and practices of individual teachers have a far greater impact on student achievement than do decisions made at the school level.

Wright, Horn and Sanders 1997, Marzano 2003

Best Practice

Effective teachers increase their students' achievement using the practices listed below, which are based on the two sources cited above. We have incorporated these practices throughout the curriculum and articulated specific ones in sidebars labeled Best Practice Tips.

• ***Asking students to identify similarities and differences.*** The years students have spent sorting and classifying in earlier grades really pay off in fourth grade as students examine number and shape sequences carefully, noting the likenesses and differences in order to find patterns and make conjectures and generalizations based on those patterns.

> ***Teacher*** *It's easy to see some ways in which these calendar markers are different. Can you find some ways in which they're alike?*

• ***Reinforcing effort and providing recognition.*** In the context of classroom discussions, you'll encourage students' tenacity with problem solving tasks. You'll also use pre- and post-assessments to identify growth with explicit concepts and skills. We often provide reminders about recognizing and celebrating students' progress toward learning goals and reinforcing the importance of their efforts.

• ***Encouraging summarizing and note taking.*** Student journals and classroom charts provide an opportunity for students to summarize information, amend their notes, and add information as they develop a deeper understanding of mathematics. We provide information about how you can model these strategies for students during whole-group discussions.

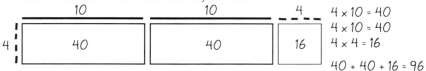

Some Strategies for Solving Big Multiplication Problems

- Build or sketch a frame and fill it in, like this:

	10	10	4
4	40	40	16

$4 \times 10 = 40$
$4 \times 10 = 40$
$4 \times 4 = 16$
$40 + 40 + 16 = 96$

- Use base 10 linear and area pieces to make an array or picture them in your head.

- Use strategies like double-doubles if you're multiplying by 4, or doubles plus one if you're multiplying by 3.

- Add the number over and over.

- Skip count, except it's kind of hard to do that if the number is very big.

- Change the number to something more friendly. 4×24 is almost like 4×25, and that's easy. It's 100. Then just take 4 away because it's really only 4×24.

• ***Assigning homework and practice.*** Home Connections directly related to the skills and concepts introduced in class are provided two or three times a week. We recommend that you grade homework assignments based on completion, not correctness, and encourage students to talk to you about any difficulties they may have encountered when completing assignments. You can assign Support Activities for additional practice as needed.

• ***Encouraging students to use and create non-linguistic representations.*** *Bridges* lessons routinely encourage students to use and create sketches, diagrams, graphic organizers, and models. The *Bridges* kit also includes Word Resource Cards that show vocabulary words along with non-linguistic representations of their meanings to help support the acquisition of mathematical language.

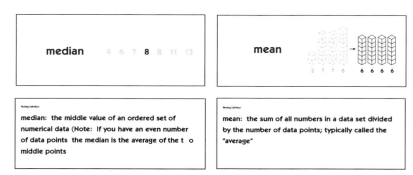

• ***Providing opportunities for cooperative learning.*** Working in pairs and small groups provides the opportunity for students to solve problems and share their strategies with other students at different ability levels. Students are also occasionally encouraged to work with students of similar abilities so that they can tailor the challenge level of certain activities to meet their own needs.

• *Helping students set objectives and providing feedback.* We encourage students to monitor their own progress and reflect on their learning goals. The pre-assessments provided for each unit give students a preview of the topics they'll be studying over the weeks that follow. If you choose to score the post-assessments, we recommend that you share major features of the scoring guide with students before they take the post-assessment and allow them to see their own scored paper afterward. You might also find it productive to have students compare the results of their pre- and post-assessments, and a Student Reflection Sheet is provided for each unit to help students evaluate their own work and set their own learning goals.

• *Asking students to generate and test hypotheses.* Fourth graders investigate patterns and number relationships, make generalizations about and classify geometric shapes, predict the results of probability experiments, and engage in scientific inquiry. Throughout these investigations, students are continually encouraged to generate and test their own hypotheses.

• *Using questions, cues, and advanced organizers to help students make connections with new content.* You'll begin many sessions by asking students to share what they notice or already know about the new content. This allows you to determine what they already know about the topic at hand and help them make personal connections to new material based on that pre-existing knowledge.

Interdisciplinary Connections

Although the teacher's role includes being alert and responsive to unexpected opportunities, it is also important that teachers plan ahead to integrate mathematics into other subject areas and experiences that students will have during the year.

NCTM 2000

In the *Bridges* program, we want students to make connections between mathematics and other fields of study, because these associations increase student engagement and enhance learning in all content areas. Toward this end, we have planned for explicit language arts, science, technology, social studies, and art activities in the yearlong curriculum.

Language Arts

Several Problems & Investigations and Number Corner workouts begin with reading a poem or book (fiction and non-fiction are both included). We also encourage you to select books from your classroom library to enhance additional sessions. Throughout the year, students will record their mathematical thinking in personal journals. We invite them to communicate their reasoning using pictures, numbers, and words. To support their acquisition of mathematical vocabulary and spelling accuracy, we provide Word Resource Cards and a personal Word Resource in the back of the student journals.

Science

Mathematicians and scientists organize information in tables, charts, and graphs and analyze the data to look for patterns and relationships. Your fourth graders will have multiple opportunities to analyze meaningful data they have collected themselves, just as scientists and mathematicians do. Students will also be immersed in scientific inquiry while investigating the physiology of birds in Unit Eight.

Tools & Technology

Calculators and computers have become some of the most widely used problem solving tools, and mathematical fluency in the twenty-first century involves being able to make appropriate use of these tools. The efficiency with which these tools complete complex calculations enhances our ability to solve problems, because we can focus on the mathematical concepts instead of the calculations. While fourth grade *Bridges* students work toward computational fluency and develop efficient mental calculation strategies, they also use calculators during some Problems & Investigations and Number Corner workouts. They are always encouraged to evaluate whether using the calculator is the most efficient problem solving method and to consider the reasonableness of their answers. Sessions, workouts, and Work Places that involve calculator use are flagged with a technology icon.

Many computer programs are available to facilitate higher-level mathematics, including calculus, data analysis, and statistics. In solving real-world problems, the computer is also a wonderful research tool, providing access to reliable sources of information and data. Computer use in *Bridges* is limited, however, because technology resources in schools vary so widely. In Unit Eight, students do have the option of using the Internet to gather more information about birds.

Through a series of experiences with measurement during Units One, Two, Four, and Eight, as well as during Number Corner workouts, students acquire firsthand experience with measuring tools including rulers, yard and meter sticks, tape measures, and containers for measuring capacity. Their measuring experiences prepare students to select the most appropriate tool for solving a problem or measuring an item, and help them develop their own referents for commonly used units of measure in both the metric and the U.S. customary systems.

Social Studies
Social skills are developed throughout the year during whole-group, small-group, and partner work. The class works together to set guidelines for their own behavior and for the creation of a community of learners. They refer to and refine these guidelines on a regular basis. Throughout the year lessons that relate to mapping, shopping, and the environment are included.

Art
Students are asked to develop their communication and artistic skills in several of the units by creating displays to share their discoveries. While exploring 2-dimensional geometry, students invent and tessellate shapes to create

works similar to those of M.C. Escher. They also work with 2-dimensional plans or blueprints of geoblock constructions, both building from their plans and sketching plans to represent simple 3-dimensional geoblock structures. The spatial relationships, rotational and reflective symmetry, congruence, and proportion they explore during Unit Four are all major elements of artistic design.

Differentiated Instruction

Differentiation is an organized, yet flexible way of proactively adjusting teaching and learning to meet students where they are and help them achieve maximum growth as learners.

Carol Ann Tomlinson

In a differentiated classroom, the teacher modifies the content (what is being taught), process (how it is being taught), and product (how the content is being assessed) based on students' readiness, learning profiles, and interests. *Bridges* provides continuous opportunities for teachers to differentiate their instruction in the following ways to meet the needs of all learners in their classrooms.

Using language, models, and symbolic notation to make meaning

Throughout the program, students are exposed to new ideas via written and spoken language, visual models, and symbolic notation. In addition, students use a wide variety of manipulatives, which provide visual and kinesthetic input, to illustrate concepts and solve problems. Students are always encouraged to solve problems and demonstrate what they know and can do using any combination of pictures, words, and symbolic notation including numbers and operational symbols. This variety of modes provides students with many ways to make sense of new material and encourages them to express their ideas in the ways that make the most sense to them.

Using flexible student groupings

Just as students have different learning styles, intelligence strengths, preferred tools, and modes of expression, they also have preferences about social interaction. Some thrive on the lively exchange of ideas that emerges in classroom discussions and enjoy games, whole-group debates, and collaborative investigations. Others prefer solitary work and the more focused conversations they can have one-on-one with a classmate or an adult. To accommodate the variety of interpersonal styles in a single classroom, and to ensure that the mode of delivery is appropriate for the topic at hand, *Bridges* provides a balance of whole class, small group, partner, and independent activities.

Whole group instruction is used to present information that everyone needs to know or to share strategies that will be valuable to all. While working as a whole group, everyone benefits when classmates share conjectures, generalizations, mathematical insights, or problem solving strategies. The teacher can also extend students' thinking by asking carefully planned questions. To the extent that it raises the level of everyone's thinking, whole group work in math is analogous to read-aloud time in language arts, when the teacher reads material that is slightly more difficult than what students are capable of reading independently.

Small group and partner activities provide more active engagement and interaction, ensuring that all students have the chance to discuss their thinking and challenge one another. Individual work helps provide evidence of what each student understands and gives more introverted students the time and space to make their own discoveries and come to their own conclusions.

Using students' interests, strengths, and needs as the basis for planning

Because much of the work in the units and Number Corner revolves around problem solving, you have almost daily opportunities to learn more about students' preferences, learning styles, strengths, and areas of need. Students are continually encouraged to develop their own strategies and are frequently given the opportunity to choose their own tools and modes of communication. You can use the information you gather from students' written work and discussions to plan your instruction to meet their particular needs.

Providing multiple access points for each activity

Bridges challenges students of varying abilities by providing multiple access points for each activity. For example, many of the lessons in Unit Seven ask students to describe and extend tile patterns. All students are encouraged to make generalizations about these patterns, but some will continue to build with tile while others will move more quickly to numbers based on the generalized patterns and functional relationships they notice. The consistent use of models and sketches provides access and deeper understanding to all.

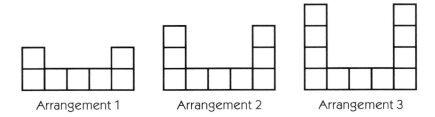

Arrangement 1   Arrangement 2   Arrangement 3

Students *It's a growing pattern!*

It gets taller and taller.

It looks like an upside down table with legs that get longer and longer, except they're sticking up.

There are always 5 on the bottom.

It's like two towers that are 1 tile high, then 2 tile, than 3 tile, but there's always 5 on the ground floor.

Teacher *Plese work on your own or with a partner to figure out how many tile are in the 10th arrangement in this pattern.*

Quick Sketching	**Skip Counting**	**Creating a Formula that Relates to the Arrangement Number**
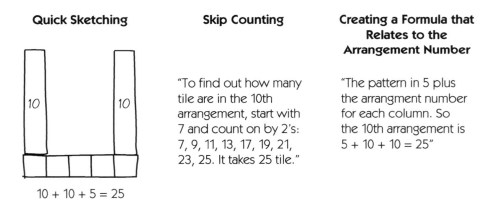	"To find out how many tile are in the 10th arrangement, start with 7 and count on by 2's: 7, 9, 11, 13, 17, 19, 21, 23, 25. It takes 25 tile."	"The pattern in 5 plus the arrangment number for each column. So the 10th arrangement is 5 + 10 + 10 = 25"
10 + 10 + 5 = 25		

Allowing for differentiated use of calculators

While some educational stakeholders fear that the use of calculators will prevent students from developing computational fluency, research, including NAEP scores, shows this is not the case. Nevertheless, many teachers use calculators in their classrooms on a very limited basis or not at all, because most students achieve some level of proficiency with paper-and-pencil calculations. There are students in nearly every classroom, however, who, no matter how hard they practice, continue to struggle with multi-digit computation long after most students have gained proficiency. This group may include students with attention deficits, memory problems, visual-spatial difficulties, auditory processing difficulties, motor disabilities, or information processing deficits.

Math educators Thompson and Sproule (2005) point out that even though the calculator is not a silver bullet, "(it) shifts the focus of attention from computation, which the calculator can do, to thinking, which the calculator cannot do, and may help students with disabilities attain levels of understanding that are equal to those of their fellow students." *Bridges* features the routine use of calculators by all students in many problem-solving situations. We also agree with Thompson and Sproule that calculator use is a reasonable accommodation for students who struggle with computation when "developing computational skills is neither the primary focus of the activity or the primary goal of the teacher in using the activity," and have found the flow chart below to be a useful tool in making day-to-day instructional decisions.

Calculator Decision-Making Flow Chart

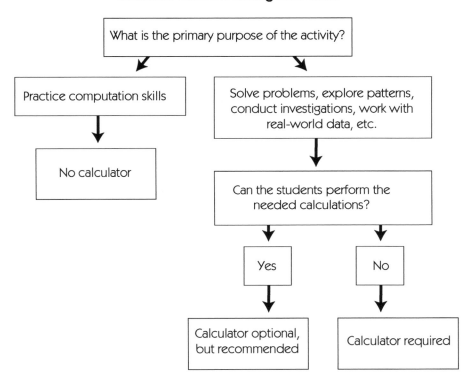

Reprinted with permission from *Teaching Children Mathematics*, copyright 2005 by the National Council of Teachers of Mathematics. All rights reserved.

Working with English-Language Learners

The basic principle underlying the different strategies for bilingual instruction can be summarized as follows: To teach an unknown concept, use the known language; to teach an unknown language, use a known concept.

Garrison and Mora

Many of the strategies used to improve instruction for English-language learners improve overall student achievement, so we encourage everyone to read this section. Those of you with English-language learners in your classrooms may find it particularly helpful.

Stages of Language Acquisition

To better understand our English-language learners, we must first become familiar with the stages of language acquisition.

• *Stage 1* — When a student enters a classroom in which a new language, for our purposes English, is spoken, that student often remains silent for some period of time. This stage is referred to as the *silent period*, and it is when the student is listening and responding using non-verbal cues. In this stage, it is important for teachers to facilitate student involvement by modeling concepts and skills using pictures and by posing questions that can be answered with "yes," "no," or the specific identification of who or where. As students sort a collection of objects, for example, we might ask them *where* their item belongs or to name a specific group by category. We sometimes think of these as low-level questions, but they are most appropriate for students in the silent period.

• *Stage 2* — The second stage is *early speech production*, when students respond with one or two words or non-verbally. *Who, what, where, when* questions, role playing, and labeling models and pictures are all teaching strategies that support students in this stage of acquiring a new language. As students construct geometric patterns, you might ask them to share what the next arrangement in the pattern looks like, encouraging them to build the arrangement with tile or cubes rather than describing it verbally.

• *Stage 3* — *Speech emergence* is the third stage of language acquisition. Students in this stage speak using phrases or very simple sentences. Asking students to predict, compare, and describe experiences, answer how and why questions, take part in group discussions, and solve problems are ways teachers can improve students' fluency with the new language when they are in this stage. When students share their strategies with another student or with a small group, they will need to answer *how* and *why* questions.

• *Stage 4* — The fourth stage is *intermediate fluency*, in which students seem more or less fluent in the new language. Teachers can support these students and help improve their fluency by asking them to analyze graphs and charts, solve problems, and evaluate situations. Students continue answering *how* and *why* questions at this stage of language acquisition. In the context of many *Bridges* lessons, you'll ask students to explain their estimation strategies or make and justify a prediction about the outcomes of a probability experiment, for instance.

Making Input Comprehensible for English-Language Learners

To increase students' fluency in the new language and their overall academic achievement, teachers must provide English-language learners with comprehensible input, that is, verbal, visual, or other sensory input they can understand. In a *Bridges* classroom, students are immersed in oral, written, and non-linguistic models for understanding the content and skills. Our goal is to establish a classroom environment that is language-rich, yet not language-dependent, in which all students can make connections with the mathematics regardless of their fluency with the English language. Toward this end, students use visual models, manipulatives, and sketches to solve problems and construct new ideas. They are also encouraged to connect spoken and written words to diagrams and models, as well as to symbolic mathematical notation.

The following nine teaching strategies help English-language learners communicate their mathematical ideas in English and support their development of different strategies for solving problems (Diaz-Rico and Weed 1995; Khisty 1995; Secada 1996; Garrison 1997; and Bresser 2003). In his work, Bresser identifies ten strategies. We have listed only nine of them here, beginning with the second strategy, because the questioning techniques suggested in his first item may or may not work well with English-language learners depending on their stages of language acquisition.

2. **Practice wait time.** After asking a question, wait for a while before calling on a volunteer. This gives English-language learners time to process questions and formulate responses.
3. **Modify teacher talk.** Speak slowly and use clear articulation. Reduce the amount of teacher talk, use a variety of words for the same idea, exaggerate intonation, and place more stress on important new concepts or questions. Model or gesture when possible to supplement the verbal discussion.
4. **Recast mathematical ideas and terms.** Mathematics has many linguistic features that can be problematic for English-language learners. Use synonyms for mathematical words, such as subtract, take away, and minus. At the same time, be aware that using too many terms simultaneously can confuse the English-language learner.
5. **Pose problems that have familiar contexts.** When a problem is embedded in a familiar context, English-language learners have an easier time understanding the problem's structure and discussing how to solve it.

6. **Connect symbols with words.** When strategies for solving problems are described, write the number sentences and point to the symbols (such as +, ×, =), stressing the words in English.

7. **Reduce the stress level in the room.** Create a low-stress environment that encourages expression of ideas, where mathematical mistakes are seen as opportunities for learning and linguistic mistakes such as incorrect grammar do not inhibit the recognition of good mathematical thinking.

8. **Use "Think-Pair-Shares."** In this activity, students think about an idea, share the idea with a partner, and then share the idea with the class.

9. **Use "English experts."** A student explains a strategy in her native language to a more capable English speaker, and then the "English expert" translates the strategy for the teacher.

10. **Encourage students to "retell."** This is when a student is asked to explain a strategy, in English, that someone else in the group might have used.

Bresser 2003

Building Bridges Between School & Home

Teachers and administrators should invite families, other caregivers, and community members to participate in examining and improving mathematics education. All partners in this enterprise need to understand the changing goals and priorities of school mathematics.

NCTM 2000

Research has shown that the home environment has a profound impact on the academic achievement of our students. It has a much stronger relationship to student achievement than does household income, parents' occupations, and parents' education. Ongoing communication is critical to the success of the parent-teacher and parent-school relationship. With the proper resources and information, parents, families, and the community can become a teacher's greatest asset and support system. In the next few pages, you'll find a variety of suggestions for helping families become more involved in their students' math education. In the appendix (pages 1.1–1.6) you'll also find a small collection of blacklines that can be made into overheads or handouts to be shared with families during the school year.

Clarifying Goals & Expectations

If you can explain your goals and purposes to families, they will be more likely to support you. Many will be eager to know what they can do to help their children work toward the fourth grade competencies and pleased to find that you'll be sending out Home Connection assignments on a regular basis. The more parents understand what you're doing in math and why, the better your rate of homework return, adult participation, and student achievement will be.

Parents need to know what will be expected of their children in math this year, so one of the things you might share with them on back-to-school night or during fall conferences is the set of Competencies & Experiences charts for Grades 3–5 in the appendix (see pages 1.7–1.12). This has worked best for us when we have introduced the charts with a brief presentation outlining the reforms proposed by NCTM and the standards our states and districts have set. Most parents identify math with computation and are usually pleased to know that their children will receive a much broader education than they did. Many, suffering some degree of math anxiety themselves, are happy to find that we're teaching for understanding as well as accuracy. We also want parents to understand that the current changes in math education have a great deal to do with pervasive changes in business and technology. Given the widespread use of calculators and computers and a growing emphasis on teamwork and collaboration in the workplace, problem solving, communication, number sense, and data analysis are basic skills critical to children's future success in school and careers. We have prepared a blackline of the U.S. Department of Labor SCANS Skills for the 21st Century, which you can use to create an overhead or handout to share with parents (see appendix page 1.1). You may notice these skills also align with the national Career and Vocational Education Standards.

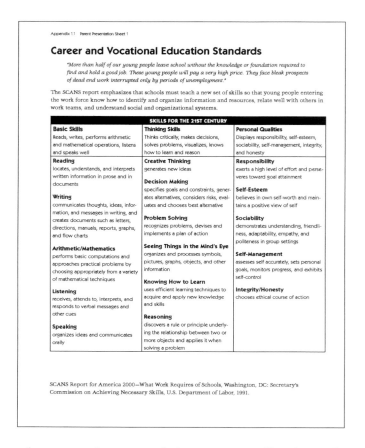

Many parents also appreciate any advice you can offer them about helping, motivating, and supporting their child's mathematical development. Toward this end, we have included in some of the Home Connections notes to families that explain the assignment and offer helpful tips. You will also find a handout in the appendix (see pages 1.5 and 1.6) that offers advice about helping with homework, enjoying mathematics in daily life, and modeling positive attitudes towards math.

Planning Successful Parent Programs

Along with the traditional back-to-school night or parent education presentations you might normally do, we recommend offering several one- to two-hour activity-based sessions during the school year that involve both students and parents. The following are several different formats we have found very successful, some which cater to parents who aren't able to attend evening presentations.

Morning Programs with Parents

Muffins for Moms and *Donuts for Dads* are two fun programs we've implemented to encourage family members to come to school in the morning hours with their children. We put a pot of coffee on, serve some muffins or donuts, and conduct some short activities that promote mathematical problem solving and communication. Games from Work Places, Number Corner, and the collection of Support Activities may be fun and manageable.

Afternoon Programs with Parents and Students

After a unit of study, we have invited parents to a *portfolio party* to celebrate students' collection of work from Work Places and Problems & Investigations. These parties are usually held immediately following our scheduled school lunch. We ask the students to present a project that we developed as a class, share their portfolio samples, and serve some snacks. We try to make sure these portfolio parties take less than an hour so that parents can attend during their lunch hour.

We have also offered presentations immediately *after school* and served cookies and milk, along with the mathematics instruction. Some of our families come to school to pick up their children, and it's a convenient time for them to plan to stay for just a little bit longer.

Game Night

If a good number of parents can attend an evening event, you might set out some snacks and a circuit of Work Place games that students are familiar with. Then, students can guide their parents through the Work Place games.

Parents enjoy seeing what their children are doing in math class, and the students love teaching their parents. You might even make math books or board games available as door prizes if your budget allows.

Strategy Night

You might also devote a night to multiplication strategies. Review the strategies briefly, and then invite students and parents to play some games together that feature the use of those strategies. The games from Work Places and the collection of Support Activities will provide some good material for such a night. You can also distribute copies of the Solving Multiplication Facts book (Blacklines 1.5– 1.7) at this event.

Tips for Success with Parents

Ultimately, your school will need to decide what options work best for your families. Don't get discouraged: try something new! Although there is no right or wrong way to work with families, we recommend you consider the following tips when planning sessions for parents.

- Offer several sessions throughout the school year at different times of day.
- Keep your sessions to one or two hours, maximum.
- Focus on specific outcomes or topics.
- Involve students as much as you can. When parents see it and hear it *from their children*, the information is more personal and relevant.
- Continue to communicate about the importance of making sense of mathematics through problem solving to help them see the value in this approach.

CHAPTER 5

Classroom & Materials Management

More than just a physical setting with desks, bulletin boards, and posters, the classroom environment communicates subtle messages about what is valued in learning and doing mathematics.

NCTM, 2000

Bridges works best when teachers implement the practices described in the previous chapter and when classrooms are set up in ways that allow students to work individually, in pairs and small groups, and as a class. Students must be able to move around, to retrieve manipulatives and other materials when they feel the need to use them, and to talk with one another as they engage in mathematical activities. We also find that when our manipulatives and materials are in good order, we can focus on our students more effectively. You will undoubtedly develop a classroom setup and system of materials management that works best for you, but we have provided the following guidance based on years of experience and feedback from other teachers.

Classroom Setup

An environment that has been carefully set up to accommodate hands-on activity, small- and whole-group sharing and discussion, and easy distribution and cleanup of manipulatives will make using *Bridges* much easier.

Furniture and Traffic Paths

During every session and workout, children will need to be able to hear each other, see each other, and share their thinking, sometimes at the overhead and sometimes at the chalkboard or whiteboard. You'll want to arrange your room so that these things can be accomplished with students seated at their desks or tables, ideally in pairs or small groups. If your room has a class set of individual desks, we strongly recommend that you arrange them so that student pairs can easily share materials, ideas, and strategies, and small groups of 4–6 students can be pulled together without moving the furniture. You'll also want to make it easy for students to access the manipulatives and materials, as well as the overhead, whiteboard, and Number Corner display.

Number Corner Considerations

Ideally, your Number Corner display will be posted on a large bulletin board that is centrally located and can easily be seen by all your students. While it's ideal to conduct some of the workouts, especially the Calendar Grid and the Calendar Collector, with the group pulled up close to the display, the space and logistics of your classroom may not permit this. If your students need to remain at their desks during Number Corner workouts, be sure that everyone can see and that there is room for students to leave their desks and come to the display to explain their thinking. If you don't have a bulletin board that's large and centrally located, consider using a rolling display board that can be moved in and out of position as necessary.

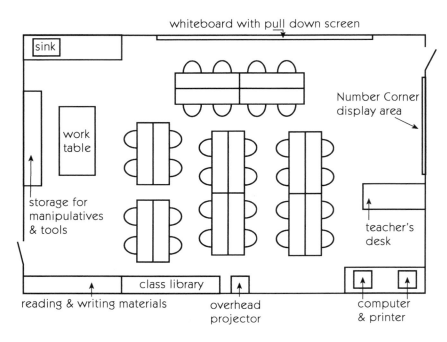

You'll also have to make allowance for the use of the overhead. Ideally, students will be able to see the screen or the whiteboard on which you're projecting your transparencies and the calendar display board at the same time.

Some teachers have found it useful to enlarge some of the record sheets that are displayed on the Number Corner board. Others prefer to make overheads of these sheets, and many have decided that these workouts are more engaging if they run class sets of the record sheets and have each student track the progress of the calendar markers and/or the growing collection through the month. We encourage you to make whatever modifications you need to make it easy for everyone in your class to see and participate.

Organizing and Managing Manipulatives

Bridges makes use of many hands-on materials, including tile, base ten pieces, geoboards, pattern blocks, wooden cubes, student clocks, and so on. (For a complete list of manipulatives, see pages 93 and 94.) We strongly recommend that you make most of these materials available to students at all times.

Fourth graders need to be able to select and use the tools they need when they need them, and they should also be held responsible for keeping the math materials organized and in good working order. For these reasons, we strongly recommend that you organize the majority of the manipulatives that have been furnished in the *Bridges* kit, along with rulers and calculators, in toolkits that can be shared by pairs of students. Although there are other options for organizing your materials (see page 81), we feel that partner toolkits are the easiest and most efficient storage system, and communicate by their very design the importance of cooperative learning and shared responsibility for classroom maintenance.

Contents of a Toolkit

If you choose to organize your math manipulatives in this fashion, each toolkit should include the following materials in the quantities specified below, which will accommodate 2 students. There are enough materials in the *Bridges* kit to create 15 toolkits; if you have many fewer than 30 students, you can either increase the quantities listed below where it makes sense to do so (as with the tile or the pattern blocks), or you can store the extra materials to use if your class size increases or if you need to replace lost items over the years.

- base four area pieces (1 strip-mat, 9 mats, 25 strips, and 30 units)
- base ten area pieces (8 mats, 20 strips, and 40 units)
- base ten linear pieces (26 linear strips (10 cm) and 40 linear units (1 cm))
- red linear units (60)
- pattern blocks (12 hexagons, 24 triangles, 12 squares, 24 trapezoids, 24 white rhombuses, and 24 blue rhombuses)
- colored tile (80)
- money value pieces (6 dollars, 2 half-dollars, 8 quarters, 10 dimes, 20 nickels, and 20 pennies)
- 2 geoboards and a bag of geobands
- 1 pattern block template
- 1 student clock
- 2 rulers marked with both inches and centimeters (you will need to provide these)
- 1 or 2 calculators (you'll need to provide these also)

Except for the geoboards, pattern block templates, rulers, and calculators, each set of materials should be packaged in a heavy weight re-sealable plastic bag in a size that's adequate but not too large. Many teachers have found the bags with zipper-type fasteners to be easiest for students to open and close. All of these materials should be placed in a larger container. This might be a clear tub with a lid (about 9" × 12" and 5" deep), an open tote with several compartments and a handle, or a simple box of some sort. The key is to choose containers that are sturdy, hold the entire set of materials well, and can easily be picked up and moved from the shelf where they are stored to students' work areas. Once you have unpacked the materials that came with your *Bridges* kit and assembled them as described above, you will have a better idea of what shape and size container will work best for you, given the storage in your classroom.

Some teachers number the toolkits and assign each double desk or table in their room a number. This encourages ownership; students who aren't careful about how they put the materials away at the end of a session have to live with the consequences the next day. Other teachers let student pairs take any toolkit from the storage shelf each day, emphasizing the importance of working as a community to keep all the toolkits in good working order.

Partner Game Packs

In addition to the manipulatives listed above, there are a few materials students will need on a regular basis to play games. Some are located in the *Bridges* kit, while others come with the Number Corner. While you can place these in the toolkits as well, we find it easier to package them separately in re-sealable zipper-top plastic bags and then store them all in a box or basket that is easily accessible to all. Each partner game pack should include the following materials in the quantities specified below:

- 5 dice (2 numbered 1–6, 2 numbered 4–9, and 1 numbered 0–5)
- 1 more or less cube
- 24 plastic game markers (12 in each of 2 different colors)
- 1 single spinner overlay

Geoblocks, Wooden Cubes, Measuring Tapes, and Measuring Sticks

The geoblocks and wooden cubes that come with your *Bridges* materials are too bulky to be stored in students' toolkits and are only needed during Unit Four. The geoblocks already come packaged in sets for use by 2 or 3 students each, depending on the size of your class. The wooden cubes come in a bucket of 1,000, and sometime before you teach Unit Four, you will need to divide them into smaller sets for use by student pairs. We recommend storing smaller sets of cubes in plastic tubs like those used for packaging spreadable margarine, salsa, or dips. There are 9 measuring tapes in the *Bridges* kit, and you'll probably want to store these with your yard and meter sticks and any other classroom measuring materials you may have.

Storage Alternatives

Although we have written the *Bridges* sessions based on the assumption that your manipulatives are organized in toolkits, we realize that not all teachers will want to use toolkits and partner game packs. Some teachers choose to package each kind of manipulative separately, creating 15 sets of base ten area and linear pieces, for instance, or 15 sets of pattern blocks for a class of 30. They place each set in a re-sealable zipper-top plastic bag and store them in their own centrally located baskets, boxes, or drawers. This kind of storage system makes it very easy for students to find a particular material, but is much less conducive to promoting student choice and responsibility than the toolkits are. You will need to do what is best for you and your students.

Other Notes about Gathering and Preparing Materials

You will need to do the following things to prepare the materials in your *Bridges* kit:

• Break the overhead and student sets of base four area, base ten area, and money value pieces apart.

• Cut or break the base ten linear pieces into lengths of 10 centimeters and 1 centimeter. Altogether, you'll need 390 10-centimeter strips and 600 1-centimeter units.

• Collect a double class set of egg cartons. Before Unit Three, you'll need to collect a double class set of egg cartons, half for use at school, and the other half to send home with students for use with some of the Home Connections for that unit. These can be either cardboard or styrofoam and depending on your storage situation and personal preference, you can cut the lids off or leave them on. These egg cartons are required for several sessions at the beginning of Unit Three, but can then be stored for use in future years so you don't have to collect so many each year.

• Label your sets of geoblocks. Before using your geoblocks, be sure to label them as shown below, using a different color permanent marking pen for each set. In Unit Four, students need the letters to identify the geoblocks as they respond to various tasks. We use a 0 in front of each letter to distinguish this set of geoblocks (set II) from sets used in other grade levels (set I is used in *Bridges* Grade 2). All the record sheets and instructions for students that include the blocks refer to them as blocks 0A, 0B, 0C, and so on.

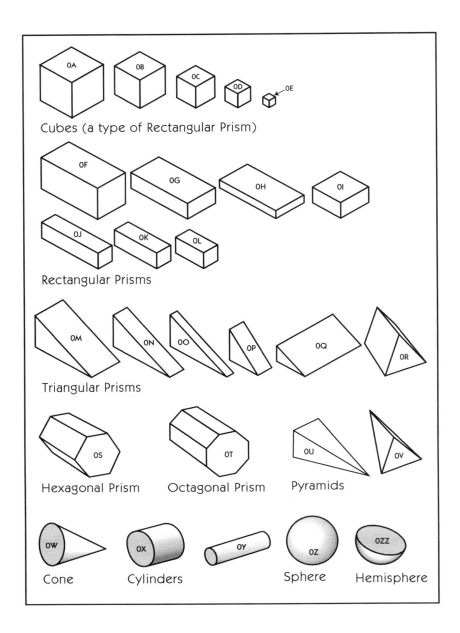

Cubes (a type of Rectangular Prism)

Rectangular Prisms

Triangular Prisms

Hexagonal Prism   Octagonal Prism   Pyramids

Cone   Cylinders   Sphere   Hemisphere

Organizing and Managing Print and Overhead Materials

Creating a System for Storing Overheads

Overhead transparencies can be stored in folders by unit, or you could place each transparency in a protective sleeve and keep them all in a binder, grouped by unit or Number Corner month. Your transparencies will last longer this way. Any overhead cards that you have cut apart can be stored in a labeled envelope or plastic bag inside the file folder or protective sleeve. Three generic overhead spinners are also provided. We recommend you store them along with your overhead pens and overhead manipulatives near your projector.

Preparing Blacklines and Student Pages Ahead of Time

Almost all of the student worksheets are available as consumable workbooks. These include the Number Corner Student Book, which contains all the worksheets students will need for the Number Corner; two volumes of Bridges Student Books, which include all the worksheets students will need during Problems & Investigations; the Work Place Student Book, which includes all the instructions, game boards, and record sheets for Work Places; a Student Math Journal; and a book of Home Connections that contains all the homework assignments for the year. Your *Bridges* kit contains a set of blackline masters that you can use to run your own copies of these books. You can purchase additional copies of any book for student use in sets of 10 or individually. In addition to these consumable workbooks, there are a few blacklines associated with most *Bridges* units and months of Number Corner, such as classroom record sheets. These are not available in workbook form and must be run as needed during the course of the units and months.

Many teachers like to organize all their materials before beginning a *Bridges* unit or month of Number Corner. You may want to copy all the blacklines and student sheets needed for a single unit or month at one time. The list of materials at the end of each introduction provides information about the copies you'll need to make for the entire unit or month of workouts.

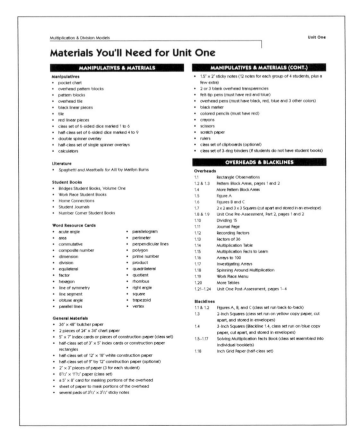

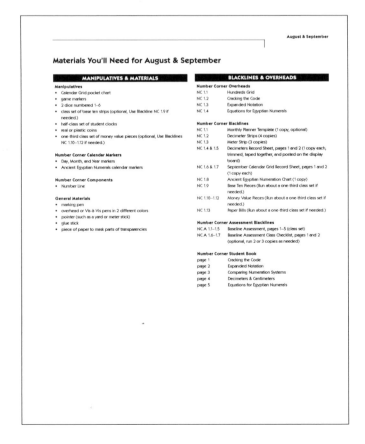

If you do this, you may want to keep the blacklines in file folders, grouped by unit or month. If students are not using their own consumable Bridges Student Books, Work Place Student Books, Number Corner Student Books, Student Math Journals, or Home Connection books, you can run the necessary pages from these books ahead of time and group them by session, workout, or Work Place.

LOCATION OF BRIDGES BLACKLINES		
Blacklines for	**Located in**	**Identified by**
Problems & Investigations	Bridges Student Books Blacklines	Page number
	Bridges Blacklines	Unit and order of use
Unit Assessments		
Work Place Log	Work Place Student Book Blacklines	Page number
Work Place Instructions		
Work Place Game Boards and Record Sheets		
Home Connections	Home Connections Blacklines	Page number
Number Corner Workouts	Number Corner Blacklines	Month and order of use
Number Corner Assessments		
Support Activities		Suggested order of use
Instructional Considerations for Support Activities		
Number Corner Record Sheets and Sheets for Independent Practice	Number Corner Student Book Blacklines	Page number

Organizing Consumable Books for Student Use

Purchasing a class set of each consumable workbook (Number Corner Student Book, 2 volumes of Bridges Student Books, Work Place Student Book, Student Math Journal, Home Connections) is the easiest solution to organizing the student worksheets for some districts. Many districts have discovered that purchasing the workbooks not only saves teachers time, but is also more cost effective than running the copies themselves.

If you purchase an entire class set of every consumable book, you'll need to come up with a way to distribute them and help students keep them organized in their desks. We suggest providing each student with a small wallet folder, which will protect their books and prevent them from getting lost in the desks. If you can, get plastic folders for enhanced durability.

We recommend that students keep only these three books in their wallet folders: the Number Corner Student Book, Student Journal, and one volume of the Bridges Student Book at a time. When a lesson calls for a book, students can retrieve them from their folders. Each book is coded with a shape in the top right-hand corner of the cover, so you can ask students to get out their "triangle" books, for example, if the lesson requires them to use their Bridges Student Books. For easy retrieval, encourage students to keep the shapes at the opening end of their folders so they can identify each book quickly and easily.

We recommend keeping the Work Place Student Books and Home Connections in a central location, since they are used less frequently than the other books. When it is time for students to do Work Places, they can retrieve their books from this central location and get started. When a Home Connection is assigned, students can retrieve their Home Connections books and take them home to complete the assignment. If you're not comfortable sending the Home Connections books home, show your students how to tear out the pages for each assignment carefully along the perforations so that they can take home only those pages that are assigned that night. Some students will invariably need your help to tear out the pages without ripping them in the process.

So that students don't have to spend a lot of time looking for their own Work Place Student Books and Home Connections books, store them in an orderly way. You might file them in alphabetical order. On the other hand, if you have a large class, you might divide them into groups named by color: the red group, the blue group, and so on. Then you can use stickers to color code the books of students in each group: for example, all of the students in the red group would get a small red sticker on the covers of their Home Connections and Work Place Student Books. You can then store all the red group's books together, all the blue group's books together, and so on, perhaps using colored folders. Then when the time comes for students to retrieve their books, a member of each group can distribute them, or students can search for their own books among only their small group's books, instead of through an entire class set.

Organizing Worksheets in Binders or Folders

If you aren't able to purchase class sets of the consumable books, we strongly recommend that you run a set of each book for each student before school starts and either comb-bind them separately or place the pages in a 1-inch 3-ring binder with dividers between each book. Teachers who prefer to have students organize their work in binders may favor this option.

If you prefer not to use binders, you could get a pocket folder for each student and have students use them to store the numerous worksheets they'll be working on in the course of any given unit. Papers will move in and out of this folder frequently, as students will be turning them in and getting new ones all the time.

Storing Assessments and Work Samples

No matter how you handle consumable books or loose worksheets, prepare a file folder for each student in which to store assessments and work samples. These folders are similar to writing portfolios and are usually kept by teachers in their own files and shared with students if and when they need to pull collections of work together to share during student-led conferences, portfolio nights, and so on. We use these collections to share with parents during conferences and also to write report cards.

Materials Organization Charts

We provide the following organizational chart to help you get started, knowing that teachers will devise systems of organization that work best in their own classrooms. This guide is meant to be a starting place as you begin to organize a year's worth of materials.

UNITS			
		How to store/organize	
Material	**Location**	**If using blacklines**	**If using a class set of consumable books**
Overheads	Bridges Overheads	In file folders or binder sleeves organized by unit	
Blacklines	Bridges Blacklines	Copies in file folders organized by unit, masters stored in a binder or folder	
Assessment Blacklines		Copies in file folders organized by unit, masters stored in a binder or folder	
Bridges Student Book pages	Bridges Student Book, Volumes One and Two*	Copies in students' math binders or in file folders organized by unit, masters stored in teacher's books	In students' own wallet folders
Student Math Journal	Student Math Journal	Copies of entire journal in students' math binders, masters stored in teacher's book	In students' own wallet folders
Work Place Student Book pages	Work Place Student Book	Copies in students' math binders or in file folders organized by unit, masters stored in teacher's book	In central location
Home Connections	Home Connections	In file folders organized by unit, masters stored in teacher's books	In central location

		NUMBER CORNER	
		How to store/organize	
Material	**Location**	**If using blacklines**	**If using a class set of consumable books**
Overheads	Number Corner Overheads	In file folders or binder sleeves organized by month	
Blacklines	Number Corner Blacklines	Copies in file folders organized by month, masters stored in a binder or folder	
Assessment Blacklines		Copies in file folders organized by month, masters stored in a binder or folder	
Support Blacklines		Masters stored in a binder or folder (run copies as needed)	
Number Corner Student Book pages	Number Corner Student Book	Copies in students' math binders or in file folders organized by month, masters stored in a binder or folder	In students' own wallet folders

* The Bridges Student Book comes in two volumes. The first volume of used in the first half of the year with Units One–Four, and the second volume is used in the second half of the year with Units Five–Eight. Make only the current volume available at a time.

What About Work Places?

Work Places are partner games and activities designed to help students consolidate and extend their understandings of the skills and concepts being taught in a particular unit. All told, there are 21 Work Places in the fourth grade *Bridges* program, two in Units One; three in Unit Two and Seven; five in Unit Three; four in Unit Four and Six; and none in Units Five and Eight. Most of the Work Places are games. Each new Work Place is introduced to the whole class in the context of a Problems & Investigations lesson, and students are then provided with time to play the game in pairs at the end of that session. After two or three games or activities have been introduced in this fashion, students are usually given a day or two to revisit the new Work Places during special Work Place sessions that occur every 3 to 4 weeks over the course of the school year.

If your students had *Bridges* in an earlier grade, Work Places will be familiar to them. The first time you do Work Places with your fourth graders, though, you might explain that Work Place sessions this year are very special math days in which students will have the opportunity to play some of the games and immerse themselves in some of the activities you've been doing together in class. While you'll set the work targets, they will set their own pace and choose the order in which they do the games and activities.

Returning *Bridges* students may remember that their teachers organized the Work Place materials in baskets for them. This year, they'll be responsible for gathering the materials they need from the toolkits and partner game packs, managing their own record sheets, keeping everything well-organized, and maintaining the kind of behaviors that make these activity periods fun for everyone, including the teacher. Instead of moving from table to table to do the different activities, students will have everything they need right at their desks so that they can concentrate fully on interacting with their partners and enjoying the practice and challenge each game or activity has to offer.

In our own classrooms, we like to open Work Place sessions by calling students' attention to the Work Place Menu overhead, which we have filled in to show a list of the Work Places that will be in use during the session, along with what needs to be completed that day. The example below is from Unit One.

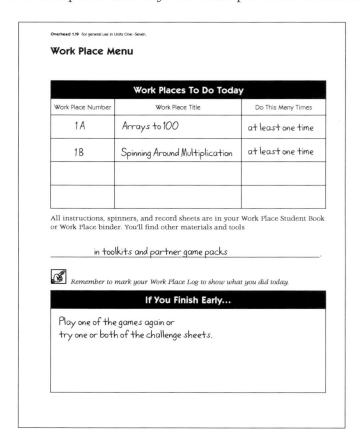

In general, the menu helps to keep everyone on track. Some children will get far more done than others, but it helps students to know what the minimal requirements are. If the menus suggested in the Work Place sessions in Units One, Two, Three, Four, Six, and Seven seem out of line with your students' capabilities, you'll need to modify them accordingly (and you may need to adjust them for certain individuals in your class no matter what). One of the reasons most students enjoy Work Place sessions so much, however, is that although we set the work targets, they get to set their own pace and do the games and activities in any order they choose.

If some students complete all the required tasks for a Work Place session, there's still plenty to do. Most of the Work Places are games that can be played again and again. Almost all of them feature extra challenges—either more challenging versions of the games or worksheets to be completed in conjunction with the games. In a few cases, we have included optional challenge Work Places as well. You might also have students revisit Work Places that were introduced in earlier units. For example, Missouri Squares is introduced during Unit Four, but students enjoy playing it long after the geometry unit is finished.

Managing the Work Place Paperwork

While a couple of the Work Places don't require students to record any work, most involve record sheets. As mentioned earlier, the easiest option is to purchase a class set of Work Place Student Books so that you can make one available to each student. (Your *Bridges* kit includes blackline masters for the entire Work Place Student Book.) This book includes enough copies of each record sheet so that students can visit each Work Place several times. If you anticipate that students may visit Work Places more than that, you can run extra copies of the record sheets as needed. The Work Place Student Book also includes a log that students can use to keep track of when they have completed each of the 21 Work Places during the year.

Work Place Student Book
NAME _____

Work Places Log page 1 of 2

Initial and date one of the boxes each time you play a Work Place game or complete a Work Place activity.

Work Place	1st Time	2nd Time	3rd Time
1A Arrays to 100			
1B Spinning Around Multiplication			
2A Moolah on My Mind			
2B More or Less Multiplication			
2C Four 4's			
3A Dozens of Eggs			
3B Fractions of a Foot Scavenger Hunt			
3C Colored Tile Fractions			
3D Remainders Win			
3E Line 'Em Up			
4A Missouri Squares			
4B Area Bingo			
4C Mosaic Game			
4D Many Faces			
6A Decimal More or Less			
6B Fractions, Decimals & Dollars			
6C Round & Add Tenths			
6D Decimal Race to Three			

Work Place Student Book
NAME _____

Work Places Log page 2 of 2

Initial and date one of the boxes each time you play a Work Place game or complete a Work Place activity.

Work Place	1st Time	2nd Time	3rd Time
7A Odd One Out			
7B What's My Rule			
7C What's Missing? Bingo			

If you aren't able to purchase a classroom set of the Work Place Student Books, we recommend that you run a class set of every page and comb-bind them to create a complete Work Place Student Book for each child at the beginning of the year.

What is the teacher's role during Work Place time?

Keep in mind that although we often provide record sheets to help students organize their thinking or track their progress through a game, Work Places are process-oriented activities. You'll want to check students' work on their record sheets, but remember that their work may not be as neat or organized as you might wish it to be. To gather more information about what they know and can do, take the time to talk with students about their work and to observe them as they complete Work Places. For Work Places that do not include record sheets, you can initial students' Work Place Logs to indicate that you have observed them demonstrate understanding of a particular concept or skill while playing the game.

We sometimes find that we need to re-teach activities to small groups of students during Work Place sessions. This is relatively easy to do if we've established our routines carefully in the first few weeks of school. Work Places, in fact, provide us with some of our very best opportunities to observe and work with individuals and small groups throughout the year, allowing us to differentiate our instruction to meet the needs of all our students.

What about student behavior during Work Places?

Although class chemistry and student behavior vary from year to year, most students love Work Places and will do what they need to in order to keep their privileges. Our rules are simple and involve safety, respect, and noise level. Refer to the class chart you'll generate in Unit One, Session 1, frequently to establish the ground rules.

How to Be a Community of Math Learners

- Listen to others and respect their thinking.
- Ask thoughtful questions.
- Disagree with others in a respectful way.
- Volunteer your ideas in group discussions.
- Don't be afraid to struggle with challenging ideas and problems.
- Know that it's okay to be confused. Confusion leads to new learning.
- Enjoy discovering new things about math.

Students who might be disruptive in some situations are often drawn into the activity, challenge, community, and camaraderie of Work Places. If we need to provide more structure or direction for certain students at times, though, we don't hesitate. For some, this means moving out of the general flow to a quiet location with an activity they can complete by themselves. For others, it means direction to a particular activity for a set amount of time. Sometimes, a careful choice of partners makes a difference. In general, we do what we need to keep things running smoothly for all students, rather than penalizing the group for the behavior of a few.

Required Materials

Your Grade 4 *Bridges in Mathematics* package contains almost everything you'll need to conduct a year's worth of sessions and workouts for a class of 30. The charts on the following pages provide details about everything in the *Bridges* package, as well as a few materials you'll need to provide. In addition to helping you with the initial setup, the charts can also be used at the end of each year to inventory manipulatives and other components. If an item is sold separately, we have listed the catalog number. You can obtain a catalog by calling (800) 575–8130 or visiting our Web site at www.mathlearningcenter.org.

Teachers Guides, Books & Ancillary Materials

ITEM	QUANTITY	CATALOG NUMBER
Teachers Guides		
Getting Started	1	B4TG
Bridges Teachers Guides, Volumes 1–4	4 volumes	
Number Corner Teachers Guide, Volumes 1 and 2	2 volumes	B4NCTG
Bridges Ancillary Materials		
Bridges Blacklines	1	B4TG-B
Bridges Overheads	1 set	B4OH
Bridges Student Book Blacklines*	1	B4SB-B
Work Place Student Book Blacklines*	1	B4WMSB-B
Student Math Journal Blacklines*	1	B4SJ-B
Home Connections Blacklines*	1	B4HC-B
Grade 4 Word Resource Cards	1 set	B4WR
Bridges Manipulative Kit (see p. 93)	1 kit for a class of 30	B4M
Spaghetti and Meatballs for All: A Mathematical Story	1 copy	SMFA
Once upon a Dime: A Math Adventure	1 copy	OUD
A Remainder of One	1 copy	AROO
Sea Squares	1 copy	SEASQU
Birds: Nature's Magnificent Flying Machines	1 copy	BIRDS
Number Corner Ancillary Materials		
Number Corner Blacklines	1 set	B4NCTG-B
Number Corner Overheads	1 set	B4NCOH
Number Corner Student Book Blackliines*	1	B4NCSB-B
Calendar Markers	12 Month Markers 7 Day Markers 10 Year Markers 9 sets of 31 Calendar Markers • Aug. & Sept.–Ancient Egyptian Numerals • Oct.–Base Four • Nov.–Tumbling Triangle • Dec.–Colors • Jan.–Night & Day • Feb.–Function Machine • Mar.–Equivalent Fraction • Apr.–Perimeter Puzzle • May & Jun.–Map Coordinates	B4NCCM
Number Corner Components	Blank Number Line	B4NCMC
Number Corner Manipulative Kit	1 kit for a class of 30	See list on p. 94

*indicates that these materials may be purchased separately as consumables

Bridges Manipulatives

MANIPULATIVE	QUANTITY	CATALOG NUMBER
Items included in Bridges Manipulative Kit		
overhead tile	1 set	T4OH
black linear units for use with the overhead tile	1 set	LU
pattern blocks	8 sets	PPBT
overhead pattern blocks	1 set	PBO
base four overhead pieces	1 set	PG40
base four area pieces	15 sets	PG4PA
base ten area pieces	30 sets	PGT
base ten linear pieces	1 classroom set	PLT
red linear units	30 sets	LUR
clear 7-inch square geoboards	30	GBC
overhead dice	1 pair	D6O
spinner overlays	1 set includes single, double, and triple	SPOH-TEMP
spinner overlays (single)	15	SPOHS
centimeter cubes	1 bucket of 1000	CW-1CM
geoblocks set II	10 sets	GEOS2
measuring tapes showing centimeters and inches	9	MTC
money value pieces	15 sets	MONVPPA
pattern block templates	30	PBT30
color tile	3 sets	T400T
Required Items Not included in Bridges Manipulative Kit		
calculators (We recommend the TI-108 because it is kid-friendly and durable.)	15–30	TI01
standard pocket chart	1	SPC
rulers, marked in both centimeters and inches	30	RLC

Number Corner Manipulatives

MANIPULATIVES	QUANTITY	CATALOG NUMBER
Items Included in Manipulative Kit		
large Calendar Grid pocket chart	1	LCGPC
overhead base ten pieces	1 set	OH10
overhead money value pieces	1 set	MONVPO
capacity containers (quart/liter bottles)	4	BOTQT
1-cup liquid measuring cup	1	QZ77
plastic funnel	1	FUNNEL
dice • 2 numbered 1–6 • 2 numbered 4–9 • 1 numbered 0–5 • 1 more/less	15 sets	D45NUM
game markers	1 bag of 400	M400
student clocks	15	DIALS

Classroom Items

For your planning convenience, we provide a list of materials needed for each unit and month of Number Corner at the end of every introduction. All sessions and workouts also include a list of the specific materials, including quantities, you'll need to conduct them. You probably have many of the supplies you'll need for day-to-day instruction in your classroom already. They include:

- marking pens
- chart paper
- several yardsticks or meter sticks
- construction paper
- butcher paper
- copier paper
- heavy yarn
- transparent tape
- masking tape
- 3″ × 5″ index cards
- paperclips
- pencils
- scissors
- crayons
- colored pencils
- glue
- glue sticks
- sticky notes

You'll also need specialized supplies that you might not already have. We've itemized them below.

- a double class set of egg cartons, either paper or styrofoam
- an overhead projector
- at least one box of blank transparencies
- baskets, boxes, or re-sealable plastic bags for packaging manipulatives
- class set of file folders to hold student assessments and work samples (for teacher's use)
- class set of 3-ring binders if you are not using individual student books
- class set of pocket folders for students to use a work folder if desired

Optional Materials

The *Bridges* package may be supplemented with additional materials such as class sets of student books and Spanish-language student and parent materials. Contact The Math Learning Center for details.

Classroom Materials

- 1 clipboard per student (optional but very useful)

Consumable Student Books

Single copies or sets of 10 available.

- Bridges Student Books, Volumes One and Two
- Work Place Student Books
- Student Math Journals
- Home Connections
- Number Corner Student Books

Translations

We offer Spanish translations of some student and parent materials. Please see the current Math Learning Center catalog or Web site for more details.

CHAPTER 6

Assessment & Evaluation

It is important that assessment tasks be worthy of students' time and attention. Activities that are consistent with (and sometimes the same as) the activities used in instruction should be included. When teachers use assessment techniques such as observations, conversations and interviews with students, or interactive journals, students are likely to learn through the process of articulating their ideas.

NCTM, 2000

Assessment is the process of gathering evidence about students' knowledge of and ability to use mathematics. Once collected, this evidence allows us to make instructional decisions based on students' strengths and needs. Before we can collect the evidence, we must first have a clear idea of what skills and understandings we want to assess and what the most effective ways to assess them are. In this chapter, we describe the competencies and experiences we expect students to have by the end of fourth grade, the wide array of assessments that are include in the Grade 4 *Bridges* program, and some different ways you can evaluate students' work and use those results.

Competencies and Experiences

As elementary teachers, we are especially aware that real growth and true understanding in any area, including math, takes a lot of time and occurs at different rates for different children. Nevertheless, we can set certain goals for our students, specifying which skills and concepts we can reasonably expect them to be proficient with by the end of each grade level. We refer to these as competencies, and they are the benchmarks around which we have organized our instruction, assessment, and evaluation of students' progress. The competencies we have identified for grades 3 through 5 are based on our experiences with students, as well as a close reading of the NCTM standards and standards from several states. We have specified competencies in six different areas—number sense and numeration, computation, algebraic thinking, data analysis and probability, measurement, and geometry—and laid them out on charts like the one shown on the next page. They reflect a considerable amount of mathematical breadth and depth. Students must be fluent with their multiplication facts and well on their way to fluency with division facts by the end of fourth grade. They must be able to add and subtract comfortable with multi-digit numbers and have developed efficient strategies for multiplying 2- and 3-digit numbers by 1-digit numbers. They must have a good sense of fractions and decimals and understand the connection between the two. They must also be able to collect data; construct, interpret, and analyze charts, tables, and graphs; and be able to describe and predict the possible outcomes of a simple probability experiment in quantitative terms. Furthermore, they must have a good understanding of area, perimeter, line and rotational symmetry, and congruence, and be moving in the direction of making not just observations, but also informal deductions about 2- and 3-dimensional shapes. We can't expect all children to achieve all of these goals by the end of the year, but they must serve as the foundation for our instruction and assessment. We can understand what our students do and don't know and adapt our instruction to help them all get closer to meeting these learning goals.

On the lower part of each chart, we have identified experiences. These are skills and concepts we want students to experience, but with which we don't expect them to be proficient. We also want to offer students who are working above grade level some challenging content. These experiences resurface in later grades so that a skill or concept that is simply an experience for a fourth grader may become one with which we expect fifth graders to be proficient. (See pages 1.7–1.12 in the appendix for the complete set of competencies and experiences for grades 3 through 5.)

Appendix 1.7

Grades 3–5 Competencies & Experiences page 1 of 6

Number Sense & Numeration		
Third Grade	**Fourth Grade**	**Fifth Grade**
Competencies		
• Read, write, order, model, compare, and identify place value of digits in whole numbers to 10,000. Use < and > symbols with whole numbers. Read and write tenths and hundredths as they relate to money. • Round whole numbers to the nearest 10 or 100. Know when an exact solution is required and when it's more appropriate to estimate. • Compose and decompose (e.g., put together and take apart) numbers to 10,000 by place value. Use expanded notation to represent numbers. (e.g., 3,206 = 3,000 + 200 + 6) • Locate and place whole numbers on a number line. • Understand, model, read, write, order, and compare common fractions (e.g., $\frac{1}{2}$, $\frac{1}{4}$, $\frac{1}{3}$, $\frac{1}{6}$, and $\frac{1}{8}$) using concrete models and visual representations. • Characterize numbers as odd or even in several ways. (e.g., divisible by 2, a double, a double and 1 more, etc.) Explain, demonstrate, and apply the fact that odd plus odd is even, and odd plus even is odd.	• Read, write, order, model, compare, and identify place value of digits in whole numbers to 1,000,000. Model, recognize, order, and compare common fractions (halves, thirds, fourths, fifths, sixths, eighths, tenths, twelfths, sixteenths) and decimals (tenths and hundredths). • Round 1-, 2-, or 3-digit whole numbers to the nearest 10, 100, and 1,000 for addition and subtraction problems and recognize which place (e.g., 1's, 10's, 100's, or 1,000's) will be the most helpful in estimating an answer. • Use a variety of physical and visual models to conceptualize fractions and interpret different meanings for fractions (e.g., equal parts of a unit whole, parts of a set, length, area, money, time). • Create, model, and recognize equivalent forms of common fractions and decimals to hundredths (e.g., 0.75 = $\frac{3}{4}$). • Locate common fractions and decimals to hundredths on a number line.	• Order, model, locate on a number line, and compare fractions, decimals (tenths, hundredths, thousandths), and commonly used percentages (10%, 25%, 50%, and 75%). • Round (with ranges from the nearest hundredth to the nearest ten-thousand) to estimate answers to calculations. • Demonstrate meanings for fractions in different contexts (area, set, number line) and recognize relationships between different forms such as mixed numbers, improper fractions, and decimals. • Create, model, and recognize equivalent forms of common fractions, decimals, and percents. (0.20 = $\frac{1}{5}$; 0.20 = 20%; 20% = $\frac{1}{5}$) • Explain prime and composite numbers, factors, and multiples.
Experiences		
• Explore different meanings for fractions (e.g., parts of a unit whole, parts of a set, length, area, money, time). • Explore equivalent fractions. • Explore fractions and decimals as two representations of the same quantities in the context of money (e.g., 50¢ is $\frac{1}{2}$ of a dollar, 75¢ is $\frac{3}{4}$ of a dollar).	• Explore equivalent fractions and use equivalence to compare fractions. (e.g., $\frac{3}{6}$ = $\frac{1}{2}$, so $\frac{2}{6}$ is less than $\frac{1}{2}$) • Explore concepts of prime and composite numbers, factors, multiples, and negative numbers. • Explore fractions as quotients of whole numbers.	• Understand fractions as quotients of whole numbers.

Assessment Methods

Assessment should be more than merely a test at the end of instruction to see how students perform under special conditions; rather it should be an integral part of instruction that informs and guides teachers as they make instructional decisions. Assessment should not merely be done to students; rather it should also be done for students, to guide and enhance their learning.

NCTM, 2000

There are many ways of finding out what our students know, and assembling evidence from a variety of sources will yield the most accurate picture of what each student knows and can do. We can observe children as they work in a variety of settings including whole group discussions, problem-solving sessions, and Work Places. We can converse with students as they solve problems or play games, or we can conduct more formal individual interviews. We can administer paper-and-pencil assessments before and after units to examine short-term growth in specific areas. We can also collect work samples to examine students' strategies and written communication skills as they solve different kinds of problems throughout the year. Finally, we can give paper-and-pencil tests that cover a range of skills and concepts every 2 or 3 months to look at long-term growth. You'll find all of these methods built into the units and Number Corner. By including a wide variety of assessment methods in Grade 4 *Bridges*, we promote equity and strive to enhance student learning. In this section, we examine each assessment method and identify how it is used in the *Bridges* program.

Observation, Interviews, and Work Samples

While paper-and-pencil tasks are what often come to mind when people think of assessment, we've found that observing students, talking to them, and looking over their work samples are all effective ways to gather information about what they know and can do. Particularly for students who have trouble recording their work on paper—because of language difficulties or dysgraphia, for instance—these methods of assessment provide information that we simply can't collect any other way.

Informal Observation

One of the best but least credited methods of assessing students is through informal observation. Over time, we develop intuitive understandings of children through careful observation, interaction, and relaxed attention. Experience with children of a particular age helps. After several years working with fourth graders, for example, one begins to notice patterns of behavior, things that 9- and 10-year-olds seem to say, think, or do on a regular basis. Knowledge of learning goals is also essential—the better you know where you're headed in a particular subject, the easier it is to recognize skills and concepts as they emerge in students.

Many teachers are already skilled at using informal observation as a way to assess students' reading skills. We have a good sense of what to expect in fourth graders' reading development and we know how to spot the signs that indicate students have reached particular benchmarks. By mid-October or earlier, most teachers have a pretty clear picture of their students' reading abilities based on their knowledge of the subject matter and their experiences observing, talking with, and reading with their students. By the time teachers are required to administer formal reading inventories, those assessment instruments often confirm what they have already learned about their students through careful and informed observation. Throughout Grade 4 *Bridges*, we have provided information that we hope will help you use informal observation to assess students' mathematical learning in a similar fashion.

By watching and listening carefully as students work together as a class, in small groups or pairs, or individually, you can also gather a great deal of information about their attitudes and work habits. Careful observation can help answer questions like the following:

- Who is willing to engage in problem solving and who tends to hang back, fearful of taking a risk, making a mistake, or because they're shy?
- Who is developing confidence in their abilities to solve problems and who seeks help, either from classmates or adults?
- Who tends to make generalizations and see patterns, and who works more in terms of specifics? There are children in nearly every class who seem to be hatching theories all the time. These are the students who notice that when you roll two dice numbered 1–6, you're far more likely to get an even than an odd product or that multiplying by 25's is just like counting quarters so $20 \times 25 = 500$ because 20 quarters make $5. These are often the same children who make connections when you read stories and pose comprehension questions.
- Who needs direction in various settings and who is more independent?
- Who is willing and able to collaborate, and who has more difficulty with the give-and-take of solving problems and playing games with classmates?

In addition to this information about attitudes and habits, careful observation can provide a good deal of information about students' development of skills and concepts. Throughout the program, we have listed the skills and concepts addressed in each session, workout, Work Place, and assessment. These lists should help clarify what you might look for as you observe students during these activities and as you look over any work samples you might collect.

We have also provided guidance in the text, sample dialog, and descriptions of student work to draw your attention to the kinds of things you might be attuned to throughout a session or workout.

Work Samples

Another informal method of assessment is work samples, papers completed by students in the course of normal instruction that you collect, examine carefully, and keep in individual files. Saved over the entire year, a collection of work samples can contribute substantially to your picture of each student's growth. We have used work samples in conferencing with parents and other concerned adults, and also in writing reports on students.

When a project has been designated as a work sample, you'll find it specially marked on the Unit Planner and at the beginning of the session. Taking the time to analyze these samples yields valuable information about the class as a whole and about individual children. To help you analyze student work samples, we have frequently included tips about what to look for as you examine their work.

Formal Interviews

Another particularly effective method of assessing children is to interview them individually. This technique is especially useful when you want to explore a child's thinking process, problem-solving strategies, or attitudes. The main drawback to individual interviews is the time involved. It can take several weeks to work your way through a class of twenty or more, simply because it's difficult to find the time and space to work with children individually. For this reason, we have only written one formal individual interview into the fourth grade program, designed for use during the first month of school. We suggest you use it very selectively to gain insights about students who are unable to show what they know on paper, or to make connections with students who are exceptionally shy. This interview, which is written up in Unit One, Session 7, will take 15 to 20 minutes per child. The write-up includes instructions for conducting the interview, recording children's responses, and interpreting the results.

Informal Interviews

Occasionally, you may want to conduct your own informal interviews with students who are having particular difficulties, are very quiet in class, or aren't able to show as much as they know on paper. This kind of diagnostic interview is simply a one-on-one discussion with a child, but it works best with some pre-planning. We suggest you begin with key questions and prepare your materials ahead of time, but remain flexible during the interview, adapting as needed to meet the child's needs and gather information that will be most helpful to you. The goal of such interviews is not to teach, but rather to find out where the child is in terms of concepts and procedures at a particular moment in time.

You might begin by asking the child to perform a task that you are sure she can do successfully, for instance, a triple-digit subtraction problem without regrouping like 154 – 132. Invite her to tell you, or show you, what she did to solve the problem and why. Then change something about the problem to raise the level of difficulty. For example, if a student subtracts correctly without regrouping, you could change the problem so that it involves regrouping (e.g., 154 – 137). You may want to suggest she use base ten pieces or a number line to show her thinking. Resist the temptation to teach and continue to watch and listen as the child explains her thinking process. Invite the child to explore and make connections between the paper-pencil task and the models. How does she react when she finds that her mental or paper-pencil computations yield one answer, while using manipulatives or sketches yields another? Can she explain the discrepancy? Does she self-correct during the exploration? Here are some other things to keep in mind:

- Be accepting and stay neutral as you listen to the child.
- Wait silently and do not interrupt the child's communication.
- Use cues like "show me" and "tell me."
- Avoid confirming a request for validation by stating "that's fine" or "you're doing okay."

Paper-and-Pencil Assessments

You'll find the following kinds of paper-and-pencil assessments written directly into the units and Number Corner, complete with instructions, blacklines, and thoughts about interpreting and using the results. When used in conjunction with informal and formal observations, conversations, interviews, and work samples, these paper-and-pencil tasks can be very helpful in assessing children's understanding of skills and concepts.

You'll need to balance the results of these more traditional "tests" with other forms of assessment, because they do have some limitations. While some students seem to be challenged and stimulated by test-taking, others are more anxious and may "freeze up" in the face of these tasks, no matter how relaxed we try to make the setting. It's also common to find fourth graders who verbalize far better than they write, and who may actually know far more than they can show on paper. Finally, we all have students who are not able to read and write well enough to complete some of the tasks without help. Do not hesitate to reread directions for students who are not yet reading at grade level. We also encourage you to interview and write for students who are not able to record their ideas on paper. You'll be assessing students' understanding of the mathematics, not their reading and writing abilities.

Baseline Assessment

If your district requires that you assess students to determine whether they are performing at grade level when they enter fourth grade, or if you simply want to get a sense of your incoming students' basic skills, we recommend that you use the Baseline Assessment, the first assessment in the Assessment section of the Number Corner Blacklines. If needed, you may also use this baseline assessment as an additional piece of evidence with which to diagnose students' needs and qualify them for special services. It measures students' proficiency with basic addition, subtraction, and multiplication facts, multi-digit computation, place value, probability, and data analysis.

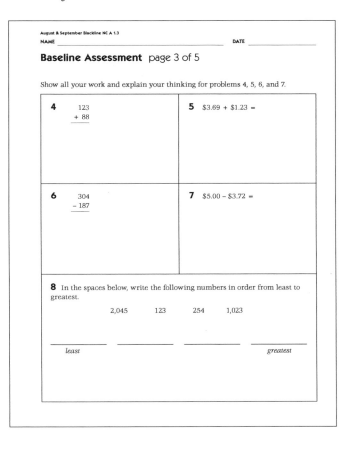

Unit Pre- and Post-Assessments

We also offer pre- and post-assessments for each unit to provide you and your students with information about their progress and growth over time. Most of the items on these assessments require constructed responses, in which students must explain their answers using words, numbers, and labeled sketches, rather than simply selecting from multiple choices, indicating true or false, or matching items. The unit pre-assessments are not intended to be scored. Instead, they are meant to provide students with information about what they'll be studying and expected to learn over the coming weeks, and to provide you with information that will help guide your instruction. Each pre-assessment is followed by a section entitled "Looking at Student Work" that describes the strategies and misconceptions you're likely to see from students at the beginning of a particular unit.

The Looking at Student Work section that follows each post-assessment includes a scoring guide, complete with annotated samples of student work where relevant. Below is an example of the scoring guide for the first problem on the Unit One Post-Assessment. You can use these guides to score each post-assessment, or you can develop your own based on your district expectations for fourth graders.

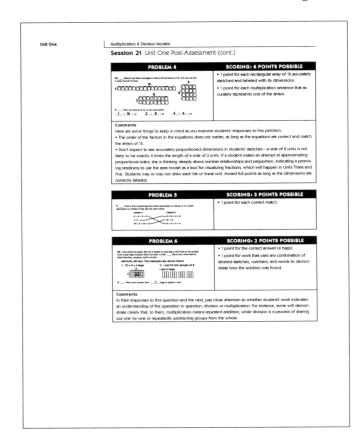

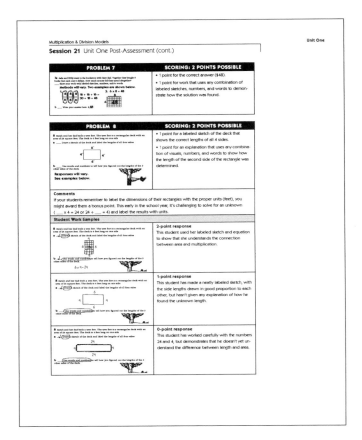

A class checklist is included for each unit pre- and post-assessment. Each item on the checklist describes the skill tested in each question, and the post-assessment checklist specifies how many points each question is worth. Once completed, these checklists provide a snapshot of how your class is doing with the assessed skills, and the pre-assessment checklist includes room for you to make notes about how you can tailor your instruction in response to students' performance.

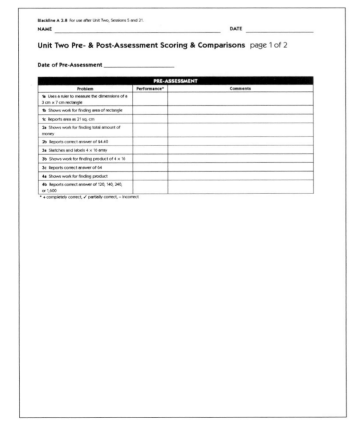

Unit Two Post-Assessment Class Checklist

Student name												
1a Uses a ruler to measure the dimensions of a 3 cm × 7 cm rectangle	1*											
1b Shows work for finding the area of a rectangle	1											
1c Reports area as 21 sq. cm	1											
2a Reports the correct answer	1											
2a Shows work in one way	2											
2b Shows work using a second method	2											
2b Second method does not involve repeated addition or skip counting	2											
3a Demonstrates an understanding of the problem	1											
3a Uses a strategy that could lead to a viable solution	1											
3a Reports a correct combination of beads	1											
3b Reports a second correct combination of beads	1											
4a Sketches and labels a 10 × 17 array	1											
4b Reports product of 170	1											
4b Shows work for finding product	1											
4c Writes a story problem that can be solved by multiplying 10 × 17	1											
5a Labels the dimensions as 12 and 14	1											
5b Shows work for computing the product	1											
5b Reports correct product of 168	1											
6a Demonstrates an understanding of the problem	1											
6a Uses a strategy that could lead to a viable solution	1											
6b Reports the correct product of 410 meters	1											
Total score / Level of proficiency**	24											

* The total possible number of points for each problem. **A Advanced/working above grade level 22–24 points (90–100% correct) P Proficient/working at grade level 17–21 points (70–89% correct)
B Basic/working toward grade level 15 or 16 points (62–69% correct) N Novice/working below grade level 14 points or fewer (61% or less correct)

Blackline A 2.10 For use after Unit Two, Session 21. Run enough copies to record the results for all students in your class.

A combination of the pre- and post-assessments checklists are also provided for each student so that you can easily compare individuals' performance on the pre-assessment with their performance on the post-assessment. Even if students have not scored particularly well on the post-assessment, you may see when comparing the two assessments that they have made substantial progress during the unit.

Blackline A 2.8 For use after Unit Two, Sessions 5 and 21.

NAME _____   DATE _____

Unit Two Pre- & Post-Assessment Scoring & Comparisons page 1 of 2

Date of Pre-Assessment _____

PRE-ASSESSMENT		
Problem	Performance*	Comments
1a Uses a ruler to measure the dimensions of a 3 cm × 7 cm rectangle		
1b Shows work for finding area of rectangle		
1c Reports area as 21 sq. cm		
2a Shows work for finding total amount of money		
2b Reports correct answer of $4.40		
3a Sketches and labels 4 × 16 array		
3b Shows work for finding product of 4 × 16		
3c Reports correct answer of 64		
4a Shows work for finding product		
4b Reports correct answer of 120, 140, 240, or 1,600		

* + completely correct, ✓ partially correct, – incorrect

Blackline A 2.9 For use after Unit Two, Sessions 5 and 21.

NAME _____   DATE _____

Unit Two Pre- & Post-Assessment Scoring & Comparisons page 2 of 2

Date of Post-Assessment _____

POST-ASSESSMENT			
Problem	Possible Points	Points Earned	Comments
1a Uses a ruler to measure the dimensions of a 3 cm × 7 cm rectangle	1		
1b Shows work for finding area of rectangle	1		
1c Reports area as 21 sq. cm	1		
2a Reports the correct answer	1		
2a Shows work in one way	2		
2b Shows work using a second method	2		
2b Second method does not involve repeated addition or skip counting	2		
3a Demonstrates an understanding of the problem	1		
3a Uses a strategy that could lead to a viable solution	1		
3a Reports a correct combination of beads	1		
3b Reports a second correct combination of beads	1		
4a Sketches and labels a 10 × 17 array	1		
4b Reports product of 170	1		
4b Shows work for finding product	1		
4c Writes a story problem that can be solved by multiplying 10 × 17	1		
5a Labels the dimensions as 12 and 14	1		
5b Shows work for computing the product	1		
5b Reports correct product of 168	1		
6a Demonstrates an understanding of the problem	1		
6a Uses a strategy that could lead to a viable solution	1		
6b Reports the correct product of 410 meters	1		

A Advanced (working above grade level) 22–24 points (90–100% correct) P Proficient (working at grade level) 17–21 points (70–89% correct)
B Basic (working toward grade level) 15 or 16 points (62–69% correct) N Novice (working below grade level) 14 points or fewer (61% or less correct)

Total Points _____   Percentage _____   Proficiency Level _____

A page is also provided each month to facilitate students' reflection on their own progress and learning goals. You can ask students to complete these sheets after looking over their scored post-assessments.

Number Corner Checkups

We have included checkups four times during the year to assess the basic skills covered in Number Corner. These skills include such things as fluency with basic facts, multi-digit computation, making measurement conversions, figuring elapsed time, adding and subtracting with money, understanding fractions and decimals, and analyzing graphs. These checkups provide fewer opportunities for students to write about their thinking, so you may need to interview a few of your students about their work on these assessments to get a clearer picture of what they know and can do.

For each checkup, we have included a class checklist. Each item on the checklist describes the skill tested in each question on the checkup. Once completed, the checklist provides a snapshot of how your class is doing with the assessed skills, both as a group and individually. These checklists are optional, but many teachers find them to be a useful tool. After reviewing the results of each Checkup, you can select Support Activities from the back of the Number Corner Blacklines to use with students who need more practice with specific skills.

Number Corner Checkup 1 Class Checklist

Student Names										
1 & 2 completes ___ out of 40 addition and subtraction facts in 2 minutes										
3 identifies the value of 8 in 1,892 as 800										
4 identifies the number 2,600										
5 converts meters to centimeters										
6 identifies an appropriate unit of liquid measure										
7 completes _____ out of 40 multiplication facts in _____ minutes										
8a adds 2- or 3-digit numbers with regrouping										
8b explains work										
9a subtracts 2- or 3-digit numbers with regrouping										
9b explains work										

October Blackline NC.A 2.5 Run as many copies as you need to record the results for your whole class.

Assessments Through the Year

The chart below identifies all the different assessments that have been written into the fourth grade program and specifies the skills and concepts examined each time. In our own classrooms, we keep these pieces dated and filed chronologically for each student. We use the files when we conference with parents and write report cards. Children pull pieces from their files to share with parents during student-led conferences. Students can also use these collections to help create portfolios.

BRIDGES YEARLONG ASSESSMENT PLAN	Basic Facts	Multi-Digit Computation	Money	Fractions	Decimals	Algebraic Concepts	Geometry	Measurement	Telling Time & Elapsed Time	Data Analysis	Probability
NUMBER CORNER INTRODUCTION											
Baseline Assessment	✓	✓	✓	✓					✓		
UNIT ONE											
Pre- and Post-Assessment, Sessions 2, 7, and 21	✓		✓				✓	✓			
Individual Interview, Session 7	✓	✓		✓							
Work Samples: Sessions 4, 8, 10	✓	✓	✓								
UNIT TWO											
Pre- and Post-Assessment, Sessions 5 & 21	✓	✓	✓					✓			
Work Samples: Sessions 14 and 19	✓	✓									
OCTOBER NUMBER CORNER											
Checkup 1	✓	✓	✓					✓	✓		
UNIT THREE											
Pre- and Post-Assessment, Sessions 2 & 20		✓	✓	✓				✓	✓		
Work Samples: Sessions 8, 16, 17		✓									
UNIT FOUR											
Pre- and Post-Assessment, Sessions 3 & 21							✓	✓			
Work Samples: Sessions 5, 7, 8, 16, 18	✓	✓					✓	✓			
JANUARY NUMBER CORNER											
Checkup 2	✓	✓		✓	✓		✓	✓	✓		
UNIT FIVE											
Pre- and Post-Assessment, Sessions 1 & 18										✓	✓
Work Samples: Sessions 4, 11, 15, 17		✓								✓	✓

BRIDGES YEARLONG ASSESSMENT PLAN	Basic Facts	Multi-Digit Computation	Money	Fractions	Decimals	Algebraic Concepts	Geometry	Measurement	Telling Time & Elapsed Time	Data Analysis	Probability
UNIT SIX											
Pre- and Post-Assessment, Sessions 1 & 22		✓	✓	✓	✓						
Work Samples: Sessions 3, 9, 10, 11, 17		✓	✓	✓	✓						
MARCH NUMBER CORNER											
Checkup 3	✓	✓		✓	✓	✓	✓			✓	✓
UNIT SEVEN											
Pre- and Post-Assessment, Sessions 4 & 14		✓				✓	✓				✓
Work Samples: Sessions 1, 3, 7, 11, 13		✓				✓	✓				✓
UNIT EIGHT											
Pre- and Post-Assessment, Sessions 1 & 19		✓						✓		✓	
Work Samples: Sessions 6, 7, 8, 18		✓						✓		✓	
MAY & JUNE NUMBER CORNER											
Checkup 4	✓	✓								✓	✓

Using Assessment Results

To maximize the instructional value of assessment, teachers need to move beyond a superficial "right or wrong" analysis of tasks to a focus on how students are thinking about the tasks. Efforts should be made to identify valuable student insights on which further progress can be based rather than to concentrate solely on errors or misconceptions. Although less straightforward than averaging scores on quizzes, assembling evidence from a variety of sources is more likely to yield an accurate picture of what each student knows and is able to do.

NCTM 2000

The assessments we've included in Grade 4 *Bridges* will provide you with valuable information about individual students and about the class as a whole. This information will help you plan your instruction and evaluate students, that is, determine where they are in relation to grade-level expectations. At that point, you can use the results to offer support where needed, provide additional challenges, and report to parents and administrators, confident that your evaluations of students reflect their true abilities, strengths, and needs.

What Is Evaluation?

Assessment and evaluation are often taken to mean the same thing, but there is an important distinction between the two. Assessment is the process of gathering information in order to make decisions. Evaluation is the process of assigning a rank, level, score, or grade to the information that has been collected. Assessment captures the situation as it exists at a particular moment or over a period of time. Evaluation places a judgment on it—advanced or above grade level, proficient or at grade level, basic or working toward grade level, and novice or significantly below grade level.

Although assessment can be enormously useful to teachers in making decisions about instruction, evaluation is generally deemed more valuable by parents, children, and administrators. Curious about what their children are doing, parents are happy to look at work samples during conferences and willing to read through descriptive checklists on report cards. But when all is said and done, many of them are more interested in how their children are doing than in what their children are doing. They want to know how their children stack up in comparison to classmates, or at least in comparison to grade-level expectations. They want to know whether they have to help their children or whether they're free to relax a bit, confident that their children are meeting the current standards.

Children, too, want to know how they're doing. Even if we set up risk-free environments in which all students are listened to and encouraged equally, and all strategies have some validity—although some are acknowledged to be more efficient than others—children compare themselves to their classmates. Unless problems are very open-ended, there's only one right answer, and some students get it more easily or more quickly than others. In spite of our very best efforts to promote cooperation and collaboration, to value the process of solving problems as much as the answers, to encourage listening and understanding, many of our fourth graders have fairly definite opinions about their own performance. In classrooms where math is taught with skill and enthusiasm, most students think they're "pretty good" or "very good" at it, but they're also curious to know how others perceive their abilities.

As people in charge of the big picture, administrators tend to be more interested in evaluation than assessment, and understandably so. Their job is to appraise programs and teachers in relation to local, state, and national standards. Their concerns often revolve around student performance on achievement tests.

This is an exciting but tumultuous period in education, and sometimes classroom teachers feel pulled in many different directions at once. We want to do the best job we can of meeting new state and district standards, but the standardized measures sometimes lag behind, testing computation and rote skills while we are teaching problem solving across many different strands. We want parents to have a full and accurate picture of their children's math performance, but this can be challenging given that math instruction in the elementary grades has changed tremendously over the past 20 years. We want all of our students to feel as if they are capable, competent problem-solvers, but we know as well as they do that some of them have a special flair for numbers and shapes, just as some of them excel at writing, being compassionate to their classmates, or running the length of the soccer field. We don't have answers to these dilemmas, but we do have a few thoughts and ideas about evaluation.

First, we suggest you grade homework (i.e., Home Connections) on completion, not correctness. You might give your students an answer key for a worksheet and have them check their own work. Ask them to repeat the missed exercises or write a short note indicating where they had difficulty and what they do not understand. Respond to these notes with assistance so that students will begin to understand that homework is another way for them to receive help. This also helps them take responsibility for their own learning and encourages them to see mistakes as opportunities for learning.

Authentic assessment tasks—such as the constructed response items on unit assessments and work samples—cannot be evaluated by simply counting correct answers. Instead, we offer annotated work samples and scoring guides to help you focus on the three main criteria you'll be evaluating in each student's work: an understanding of the problem, mathematical accuracy, and clarity of presentation. You will use these three criteria to rate student proficiency based on appropriate developmental milestones and mathematics standards.

We recommend that you share the scoring guides, or at least some of the basic criteria on which they'll be scored, with students before administering unit post-assessments. This encourages students to take the initiative to extend their thinking and communication. You can also share examples of advanced and proficient work from previous years to encourage students to strive for better performances rather than just "getting by."

Using the Results of Evaluation

You can use the results of evaluations of student work in a variety of ways. First, you'll probably want to use what you've learned about students to tailor your whole-group instruction to better meet their current needs, both by offering support where needed and by challenging students to extend their thinking. Second, the results of evaluations provide valuable information you can communicate to students and to parents or other interested adults, including administrators.

A Word of Caution About Scoring Unit Post-Assessments

In addition to offering a scoring guide for each of the unit post-assessments, we also encourage you to use the percentage of points earned to determine whether a student is working at an advanced, proficient, basic, or novice level with regard to the material on the assessment. Please remember that when we use these terms, we are referring to what we consider standard for a particular point in time during the fourth grade year, based on our own Competencies & Experiences (see appendix, pages 1.7–1.12 for more information). You may need to adjust the scoring system for a particular assessment to ensure that it reflects the expectations for fourth-graders in your district.

SCORING UNIT POST-ASSESSMENTS		
Points scored	**Percentage of Total**	**Level**
26 – 29 points	90–100%	Advanced (Working above grade level)
22 – 25 points	75–89%	Proficient (Working at grade level)
19 – 21 points	65–74%	Basic (Working toward grade level)
18 points or fewer	64% or lower	Novice (Working below grade level)

Scoring Guide for Unit One

It is critical to bear in mind that a student's performance on a post-assessment is only one measure of his or her competency with the assessed skills and concepts, and that it is vitally important to inform your judgments about individuals' progress using the many other sources of information we've outlined in this chapter. Please use the Skills & Concepts Tracking Chart (appendix, pages 1.16–1.24) to make use of additional work samples, assessments, and observational opportunities that will provide further evidence about whether students are working at grade level with these skills and concepts.

Math Skills & Concepts Tracking Chart Early Fourth Grade

Skills & Concepts	Primary Instruction		Assessment		Support
	Units	Number Corner	Informal Assessment	Formal Assessment	
Numbers & Numeration					
Reads, writes, and understands numbers to 99,999.	Unit 2, Sessions 3, 4	September Calendar Grid and Problem So In tober Calendar Grid and Number Line ember Problem So In and Number Line anuar Number Line	S pe es 2, 3	umber omer ase ine Assessment a ine A 1.3 umber omer e up 1 a ine A 2.2 umber omer e up 2 a ine A 3 Unit 1, Session	umber omer Support A. ti lbes 2, 26, 2 Additiona time wit e ember and January Number Line Games
Understands, models, reads, writes, orders, and compares common fractions (e.g., ½, ⅓, ¼, ⅛, ¹⁄₁₀) using concrete models and visual representations.	Unit 3, Sessions 1–11	October–December Calendar Collector	NCSB pages 42, 45 BSB pages 47–49, 53 ork Places 3A, 3B, 3C PSB pages 35–36, 38, 42–44	Number Corner Baseline Assessment (Blackline NC A 1.4) Number Corner Checkup 2 (Blackline NC A 5.4) Unit 1, Session 7 Unit 3, Sessions 2, 2	Additional time with Work Places 3A, 3B, 3C Number Corner Support Activities 24, 25
Basic Facts					
Knows addition and subtraction facts to 20.				Number Corner Baseline Assessment (Blackline NC A 1.1) Number Corner Checkup 1 (Blackline NC A 2.1)	Number Corner Support Activity 1 (Also see Grade 3 Support Activities 1–6)
Knows multiplication facts through 6 × 10.	Unit 1, Sessions 8–17	September–January Number Line October–January Computational Fluency	NCSB pages 6, 7, 9, 10, 12, 13, 15, 16, 22, 23, 25, 26 28, 29, 34, 35, 50 BSB pages 6, 14, 15, 18 Work Places 1A, 1B WPSB pages 6–8, 10–13	Number Corner Baseline Assessment (Blackline NC A 1.2) Number Corner Checkup 1 (Blackline NC A 2.3) Number Corner Checkup 2 (Blackline NC A 5.1) Unit 1, Sessions 2, 7, 21 Unit 2, Sessions 5, 21 Work Samples Unit 1, Sessions 4, 8, 10	Additional time with Work Places 1A, 1B Number Corner Support Activities 12–17

NCSB—Number Corner Student Book, BSB—Bridges Student Book, WPSB—Work Place Student Book

Providing Support and Additional Challenges

Many of the assessments will allow you to determine which students have met a specific benchmark, as well as those who have surpassed it and those who still need additional support to meet it. When you know which students have yet to meet an important benchmark, you can assign Support Activities that are designed to help them meet that benchmark. All of the Support Activities below are located in a separate section of the Number Corner Blacklines.

SUPPPORT ACTIVITIES		
Activity	**Name**	**Topic**
1	Spinning Around Subtraction	Subtraction facts to 20
2	More or Less Place Value	Place value to hundreds place
3	Make 100	2-digit addition
4	Race to 100 & Back	Basic addition and 2-digit addition
5	Count Down 400	2- and 3-digit subtraction
6	More or Less Addition	2-digit addition
7	More or Less Subtraction	2-digit subtraction
8	Three Turns to Win	Counting and adding money
9	Finish with $10	Adding and subtracting money amounts up to $10
10	An Hour or Bust	Telling time and calculating elapsed time
11	Get Me to the Bus on Time	Telling time and calculating elapsed time
12	Spinning Around Multiplication	Strategies for multiplication facts up to 6 × 6
13	Array Challenge	Multiplication facts to 8 × 9 with the array model
14	Multiplication Challenge	Multiplication facts to 8 × 8 with a variety of models
15	Spinning for Arrays	Multiplication facts to 8 × 10 with the array model
16	Product Bingo	Practice of multiplication facts to 9 × 9
17	What's Missing? Bingo	Practice of multiplication and division facts to 9 × 6
18	More or Less Addition Big Time	3-digit addition with regrouping
19	More or Less Subtraction Big Time	3-digit subtraction with regrouping
20	Larger Numbers on a Line	3-digit subtraction and addition with regrouping
21	Perimeter Showdown	Perimeter and area of rectangles
22	Spin & Multiply	2-digit by 1-digit multiplication
23	Remainders Win	Division with remainders
24	Fraction Race	Understanding, modeling, and comparing fractions
25	Fraction Bingo	Understanding, modeling, and comparing fractions
26	Round & Add Tens	Rounding 2-digit numbers to the nearest ten and adding 2- and 3-digit numbers
27	Round & Add Hundreds	Rounding 3-digit numbers to the nearest hundred and adding 3- and 4-digit numbers
28	Divide 'Em Up	Dividing 2-digit numbers by 1-digit numbers using models
29	Money, Fraction & Decimal Showdown	Comparing common fractions, decimals, and money amounts with models

If you know which students have met or exceeded specific benchmarks, you can provide some more challenge for them in small group and partner work during Problems & Investigations. We've included suggestions about how to challenge students throughout the text. In addition, most Instructional Considerations sections for Work Places include a challenge icon that indicates how you can increase the difficulty level for those students who need it. We recommend pairing students of similar ability levels when you introduce a new challenge for a particular Work Place. Many Home Connections and worksheets also include challenge items for those students who are ready.

Helping Students See Their Own Progress and Set Goals
Although they certainly don't want all the details, students do need a sense of where they're headed in mathematics. This is one of the reasons we have included pre- and post-assessments. Pre-assessments give students a chance to see what new content is coming up, and comparing their performance on the pre-assessment with the post-assessment allows students to see how they've improved and what they still need to work on. We find that students are often proud of their accomplishments when they see the progress they've made. Also, when students can see for themselves where they need improvement, they can set their own learning goals, with some guidance from you. Inviting students to monitor their own progress and complete a Student Reflection Page for each unit encourages them to take responsibility for their own learning.

Blackline A 1.14 For use after Unit One, Session 21.

NAME _____   DATE _____

Unit One Student Reflection Sheet

Go over your scored post-assessment, and think about these goals as you do. Think about what you did well and what you could improve.

The major learning goals for this unit were to:

- Improve geometry vocabulary and your ability to describe shapes
- Understand and use the rectangular array model for multiplication and division
- Draw sketches or diagrams to go with story problems
- Determine factors of whole numbers (build all the arrays for a number)

- Know whether a number is prime or composite
- Find the area and perimeter of a rectangle
- Use strategies (the ones we explored or your own) to solve multiplication facts you don't remember
- Label and explain your drawings clearly with words and/or numbers

1 What did you do well on this assessment and in this unit?

2 What are two goals for your mathematical learning that are important to you? (What could you improve?)

a

b

3 How will you meet each goal above?

a

b

Reporting to Parents and Administrators

One of the more powerful ways we communicate with parents and children is through conferencing and writing reports. Although your district probably determines the form and content of your report cards, you may be free to supplement with written comments, checklists, and the like. We have also provided the Math Skills & Concepts Student Report shown below (appendix, pages 1.13–1.15) to help you report students' progress to parents in greater detail.

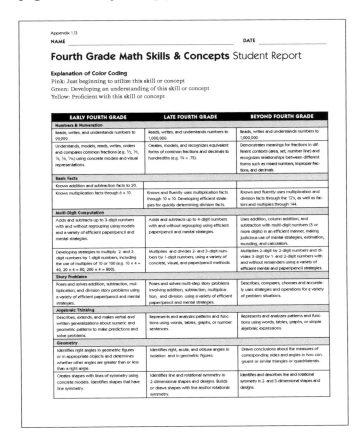

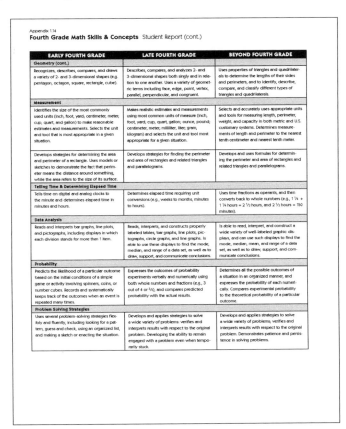

The continuum is based on the Grade Four Competencies (apppendix, pages 1.7–1.12) and reflects what you'll teach in Grade 4 *Bridges*. While it doesn't report on every competency, it gives a reasonably comprehensive picture of children's math performance in the context of grade level expectations. We have included the Math Skills & Concepts Tracking Chart (appendix, pages 1.16–1.24) to help you identify which work samples and activities will provide evidence of students' progress with each competency on the continuum.

Before using the Skills & Concepts Student Report, you may want to cross-reference it with your state grade-level benchmarks and make note of which competencies are not included in your state standards and add important state benchmarks that are not included on this continuum. By evaluating students in terms of whether they have met, exceeded, or have yet to meet state or local benchmarks, you will make these evaluations accessible and useful for school and district administrators as well.

In addition to color-coding the continuum, there is room to write a note about each child's attitudes and work habits in math, along with thoughts about any special strengths or weaknesses. During conferences, you can provide even more information for parents by sharing work samples, constructed response assessments, and pre- and post-assessments, along with the scoring guide or other standard you have used to evaluate them, as well as their child's checklist for comparing pre- and post-assessments.

CHAPTER 7

Supporting Research

The approaches to teaching and learning in *Bridges in Mathematics* are grounded in research. The following is an annotated bibliography of some of the books and articles that have most dramatically influenced the development of the program. We have included this bibliography to give you some information about the foundations of the program, as well as to direct you toward reading that you may find helpful and informative. You'll notice that some resources are a bit older than others. We began developing this program years ago, when these resources were current. We feel that their value has withstood the test of time, but we have also included more current resources that have informed the program as well.

Bennett, Albert B. and L. Ted Nelson. 2004. *Mathematics for Elementary Teachers: A Conceptual Approach*, 6th ed. New York: McGraw Hill.

> Bennett and Nelson's textbook for pre-service and in-service teachers of elementary mathematics provides a wealth of information about mathematical concepts. It includes activities that can be used with children, as well as activities that help teachers deepen and strengthen their own mathematical understandings. The textbook has an accompanying activity book that provides more extensive concept development through hands-on mathematics activities and problem solving.

Beto, Rachel. 2004. "Assessment and Accountability Strategies for Inquiry-Style Discussions." *Teaching Children Mathematics,* 10 (9): 450–454.

> This lively article, written by a practicing classroom teacher, discusses teaching and assessment strategies that boost participation and hold all students accountable for inquiry-style discussions. The article includes many intelligent and realistic tips for promoting student discourse.

Bresser, Rusty. 2003. "Helping English-Language Learners Develop Computational Fluency." *Teaching Children Mathematics,* 9 (6): 294–299.

> The author outlines ten strategies for helping English-language learners become computationally fluent. The strategies include specific questioning techniques, the use of wait time following a question, and ways for teachers to modify their speech to make it more comprehensible for English-language learners. Bresser also stresses the value of cooperative learning strategies like think-pair-share and asking some English-language learners to act as English experts for their peers.

Burns, Marilyn and Robyn Silbey. 2000. *So You Have to Teach Math? Sound Advice for K–6 Teachers,* Sausalito: Math Solutions Publications.

> This slender volume provides honest and straightforward answers to 101 questions teachers ask most frequently about standards-based math instruction. The book isn't tied to a particular math program, but teachers using *Bridges* will find clear answers and down-to-earth advice about everything from managing manipulatives to handling homework. *So You Have to Teach Math?* is particularly helpful for new teachers, teachers switching grade levels, teachers using a standards-based math program for the first time, and teachers who need to be able to provide clear but cogent explanations to parents.

Carroll, W. and D. Porter. 1997. "Invented Strategies can Develop Meaningful Mathematical Procedures." *Teaching Children Mathematics,* 3 (7): 370–374.

> The authors explore the ways in which students' invented computational procedures promote understanding. The article describes students' strategies and includes illustrations of student work.

Duckworth, Eleanor. 1987. *"The Having of Wonderful Ideas" and Other Essays on Teaching and Learning.* New York: Teachers College Press.

> In this collection of Duckworth's writings on Piaget and teaching, she writes about how to create situations and "occasions" in which learners of all ages can construct their own knowledge and understandings. While based heavily in theory, Duckworth's writing is accessible to a wide audience and uses many examples of teachers' and students' experiences in the classroom.

Fosnot, Catherine Twomey and Maarten Dolk. 2001. *Young Mathematicians at Work: Constructing Multiplication and Division.* Portsmouth, NH: Heinemann.

> In the second book in the *Young Mathematicians at Work* series, Fosnot and Dolk provide strategies to help teachers turn their third through fifth grade classrooms into math workshops that encourage and reflect real-world mathematics. They examine ways to engage and support children as they construct important strategies and big ideas related to multiplication and division. Classroom visits and student work samples help define modeling and provide examples of how learners construct models in context.

Fosnot, Catherine Twomey and Maarten Dolk. 2002. *Young Mathematicians at Work: Constructing Fractions, Decimals, and Percents.* Portsmouth, NH: Heinemann.

> In the third book in the *Young Mathematicians at Work* series, Fosnot and Dolk focus on how children in the intermediate grades construct deep understandings of fractions, decimals, and percents.

Fuson, Karen. 2003. "Toward Computational Fluency in Multidigit Multiplication and Division." *Teaching Children Mathematics,* 9 (6): 300–305.

> This article is an excerpt from a longer paper commissioned by NCTM's Research Advisory Committee to summarize the current state of educational research. This excerpt deals specifically with multi-digit multiplication and division, and provides convincing evidence that algorithms based on the area model are far more accessible to learners than the traditional algorithms generally taught to fourth and fifth graders.

Garrison, Leslie and Jill Kerper Mora. 1999. "Adapting Mathematics Instruction for English-Language Learners: The Language-Concept Connection." In *Changing the Faces of Mathematics: Perspectives on Latinos,* edited by Luis Ortiz-Franco, Norma G. Hernandez, and Yolanda De La Cruz. Reston, VA: The National Council for Teachers of Mathematics.

> In this fifth chapter of a volume on Latinos and mathematics education, Garrison and Kerper Mora discuss the "vital role of language in the development of mathematical concepts." They write about the challenges and opportunities for learning that are present in four "domains." In the first domain, both language and concepts are unknown to the student. In the second, the language is known, but the concept is unknown. In the third, the language is unknown, but the concept is known. In the fourth domain, both the language and concept are known. They outline a wide variety of strategies for making input comprehensible for students in these different domains, using familiar content to reinforce language skills and making new mathematical content accessible to students who do not yet speak the language of instruction, in this case, English.

Hiebert, J., T. P. Carpenter, E. Fennema, K. C. Fuson, D. Wearne, H. Murray, A. Oliver, and P. Human. 1997. *Making Sense: Teaching and Learning Mathematics with Understanding.* Portsmouth, NH: Heinemann.

> This book describes the essential features of a classroom that promotes mathematics understanding. These essential features include the nature of classroom tasks, the role of the teacher, the social culture of the classroom, the use of mathematical tools as learning supports, and the importance of equity and accessibility. In the chapter covering mathematical tools, the authors write, "First, tools of some kind are unavoidable and essential for doing mathematics. Second, students develop meaning for tools by actively using them in a variety of situations, to solve a variety of problems. Third, using tools enables students to develop deeper meaning of the mathematics that the tools are being used to examine."

Hufford-Ackles, Kimberly, Karen Fuson, and Miriam Sherin. 2004. "Describing Levels and Components of a Math-Talk Community." *Journal for Research in Mathematics Education*, 35 (2): 81–116.

> The authors of this article outline a number of concrete actions teachers can take to encourage the growth and development of a classroom math community, including:
> • asking questions that focus on mathematical thinking rather than answers.
> • asking students to explain their thinking while resisting the temptation to paraphrase their ideas.
> • posing problems that are open-ended.
> • inviting extended descriptions of strategies and soliciting more than one way to solve a problem, even a straightforward computation.
> • expecting students to take on central roles in discussion and giving them the physical and psychological space to do so.
> • coaching students in their participatory roles in the discourse, either as speakers or active listeners.
> • actively monitoring interactions from the side or back of the room, and giving assistance when students need clarification or support in an interaction.

Jarrett, Denise. 1999. *Teaching Mathematics and Science to English Language Learners*. Portland, OR: Northwest Regional Educational Laboratory.

> This is one of three publications dedicated to research-based instructional strategies published as part of the Northwest Regional Educational Laboratory's *It's Just Good Teaching* series. Each publication focuses on the diverse needs of the gifted, learning disabled, and English-language learners in an inclusive classroom. Jarrett writes, "To participate meaningfully in the academic discourse and abilities that are necessary to achieve the mathematics and science standards, teachers must help [English-language learners] to develop language skills that go beyond mere social fluency." The author includes suggestions for cooperative learning strategies, teaching through inquiry and problem solving, vocabulary development, and assessment strategies that link second-language acquisition strategies with other standards-based practices.

Maier, Eugene. 2003. *Gene's Corner and Other Nooks & Crannies*. Portland, OR: The Math Learning Center.

> This collection of essays by Dr. Eugene Maier, co-founder of The Math Learning Center, chronicles 50 years of experience as a mathematician and educator. Essays focus on such topics as standardized testing, current issues in education, how children learn mathematics, and the role of technology in math education.

Marzano, Robert J. 2003. *What Works in Schools: Translating Research into Action.* Alexandria, VA: Association for Supervision and Curriculum Development.

> Marzano divides the factors affecting student achievement into three categories: school-level factors, teacher-level factors, and student-level factors. In this book, he synthesizes the research and concludes that "the impact of decisions made by individual teachers is far greater than the impact of decisions made at the school level." He describes the instructional strategies that are directly correlated with increased student achievement.

Mooney, Carol Garhart. 2000. *Theories of Childhood: An Introduction to Dewey, Montessori, Erikson, Piaget & Vygotsky.* St. Paul, MN: Redleaf Press.

> This slim volume provides clear, brief summaries of theories from Dewey, Montessori, Erikson, Piaget, and Vygotsky that are relevant to work with young children. Mooney also explains how an understanding of these theories can improve classroom practices for early childhood and elementary teachers.

National Council for Teachers of Mathematics. 2000. *Principles and Standards for School Mathematics.* Reston, VA: The National Council for Teachers of Mathematics.

> This publication is the 2000 revision of the NCTM Principles and Standards, first published in 1989. A whole chapter is devoted to principles of school mathematics, which include equity, curriculum, teaching, learning, assessment, and technology. The standards also outline expectations for students' mathematical learning in four grade bands: Pre-K–2, grades 3–5, grades 6–8, and grades 9–12. NCTM outlines standards related to both content (e.g., geometry) and process (e.g., communication).

National Research Council. 2002. *Helping Children Learn Mathematics.* Washington, DC: National Academy Press.

> This book is based on the premise that all students can and should become proficient in mathematics. Mathematical proficiency involves five intertwined strands: understanding mathematics, computing fluently, applying concepts to solve problems, reasoning logically, and engaging with mathematics, seeing it as sensible, useful, and doable. According to the authors, "For all students to become mathematically proficient, major changes must be made in mathematics instruction, instructional materials, assessments, teacher education, and the broader educational system."

Schifter, D. and C. Fosnot. 1993. *Reconstructing Mathematics Education: Stories of Teachers Meeting the Challenge of Reform.* New York: Teachers College Press.

> This book brings the reader into second and third grade classrooms to observe students engaged in mathematical activity. Schifter and Fosnot use these case studies to help teachers think about how students learn mathematics and consider what it takes for teachers to learn how to

teach mathematics. They write, "No matter how lucidly and patiently teachers explain to their students, they cannot understand for their students. Once one accepts that the learner must herself actively explore mathematical concepts in order to build the necessary structure of understanding, it then follows that teaching mathematics must be reconceived as the provision of meaningful problems designed to encourage and facilitate the constructive process."

Senk, S. and D. Thompson. (Eds.) 2003. *Standards-Based School Mathematics Curricula: What Are They? What Do Students Learn?* Mahwah, NJ: Lawrence Erlbaum Associates.

This book provides an overview of many of the standards-based mathematics curricula currently being used in elementary, middle, and high school classrooms in the United States. It also attempts to answer the question of how effective these curricula are, compared to more traditional mathematics curricula, at helping students learn and understand mathematics. Numerous evaluation studies designed to answer this question are presented. In a review of the book for the *Journal for Research in Mathematics Education* (May, 2003, 34 (3): 260–265), Jinfa Cai summarized the results of these studies as follows, "Results from all of the evaluation studies reviewed appear to point in the same direction: On standardized tests measuring computational skills and procedural knowledge, students in standards-based school mathematics curricula performed at the same level as students using traditional school curricula. In addition, students in standards-based school mathematics curricula performed better than students using traditional school curricula on specifically designed tests measuring conceptual understanding and problem solving." Cai also noted a potential conflict of interest in many of the evaluation studies, "It is worth noting that many evaluation studies reviewed in this book were conducted by individuals or groups having a close association with the curriculum evaluated."

Sutton, J. and A. Krueger. (Eds.) 2002. *ED Thoughts: What We Know About Mathematics Teaching and Learning.* Aurora, CO: Mid-continent Research for Education and Learning.

According to the authors, "The purpose of this volume is to support standards-based reform of mathematics education." They provide a wealth of research and information about teaching and learning mathematics that supports a standards-based approach to mathematics instruction. The book focuses on six major topics: mathematics for all, teaching mathematics, assessment in mathematics, mathematics curriculum, instructional technology in mathematics, and learning mathematics. The book uses a question-and-answer format; the authors pose a question and then answer it from the perspectives of research and best practices. A discussion of the implications for improving classroom instruction follows each of the forty-four question-and-answer segments. The references used to answer each question are listed on the same page as the classroom implications, making them easy to find and use.

Thompson, Tony and Stephen Sproule. 2005. "Calculators for Students with Special Needs." *Teaching Children Mathematics*, 11 (7): 391–395.

Supported by current research, Thompson and Sproule argue that calculators can be used to help students with learning disabilities develop mathematical skills and understandings. They offer guidance, including a clear flowchart, to help teachers decide when and how to have students use calculators. In conclusion, they state that the calculator can be used "as a tool that can facilitate equity and inclusion and allow all students to access the full range of rich mathematics. In addition to helping students gain access to mathematical experiences that would otherwise be inaccessible to them, using a calculator can help many students with special needs increase their self-confidence, reduce their anxiety, and increase their motivation to solve mathematical problems."

Tomlinson, Carol Ann. 1999. *The Differentiated Classroom: Responding to the Needs of All Learners*. Alexandria, VA: Association for Supervision and Curriculum Development.

Tomlinson draws from research on learning, education, and change for the theoretical basis of differentiated instruction. In this book, she defines a differentiated classroom and the elements of differentiation. She describes the learning environments, instructional techniques, and standards-based assessment approaches that promote learning for all children. Her premise is that most effective teachers modify some of their instruction for students some of the time. She challenges educators to use assessment data thoughtfully to modify the content, process, and products to best meet the learning profiles, readiness, and interests of students.

Van de Walle, John A. 2004. *Elementary and Middle School Mathematics: Teaching Developmentally*, 5th ed. New York: Pearson Education, Inc.

This resource for elementary and middle school mathematics teachers focuses on how to address specific mathematical topics across the elementary and middle school grades. Each chapter is devoted to a particular topic or strand, and Van de Walle then chronicles how students' understandings of that topic or strand develop as they progress through elementary and middle school. He also suggests activities for use with students at various grade levels.

Webb, Norman L. 1999. *Alignment of Science and Mathematics Standards and Assessments in Four States.* Washington, DC: Council of Chief State School Officers.

> In his report on the alignment of mathematics curriculum, instruction, and assessment, Webb identifies and describes four levels of depth of knowledge: recall, basic application, strategic thinking, and extended thinking. He describes the learning activities and responses that characterize these levels of depth of knowledge in math and science. The cognitive demand of the NCTM standards are written at the second and third levels, and therefore instruction and assessments should be primarily at the application and strategic thinking levels so that we have aligned our practices with the intent of the standards.

Wolfe, Patricia. 2001. *Brain Matters: Translating Research into Classroom Practice.* Alexandria, VA: Association for Supervision and Curriculum Development.

> Wolfe's book is an easy-to-read guide about how the brain works in relation to learning and teaching. She compiles research from many studies and explains how the findings translate into classroom practice. The chapter devoted to visual thinking is very informative for any teacher of any subject. She writes, "Not only are visuals powerful retention aids, but they also serve to increase understanding. ... The ability to transform thoughts into images is often viewed as a test of understanding. But some people appear to process information the other way around, literally seeming to comprehend information by visualizing it. One such person was Albert Einstein, who appeared to process information primarily in images, rather than in written words or spoken language. ... One of the defining characteristics of this type of reasoning is the ability to transform abstract concepts into visual images."

Wood, T. and P. Sellers. 1997. "Deepening the Analysis: Longitudinal Assessment of a Problem-Centered Mathematics Program." *Journal of Research in Mathematics Education,* 28 (2): 163–186.

> Longitudinal analyses of the mathematical achievement and beliefs of three groups of elementary pupils are presented. The groups consist of those students who had received two years of problem-centered mathematics instruction, those who had received one year, and those who had received textbook instruction. Comparisons are made for the groups using a standardized norm-referenced achievement test from first through fourth grade. Next, student comparisons are made using instruments developed to measure conceptual understanding of arithmetic and beliefs and motivation for learning mathematics. The results of the analyses indicate that after two years in problem-centered classes, students have significantly higher results on standardized achievement measures, better conceptual understanding, and more task-oriented beliefs for learning mathematics than do students who

received textbook instruction. In addition, these differences remain after problem-centered students return to classes using textbook instruction. Comparisons of pupils in problem-centered classes for only one year reveal that after returning to textbook instruction, these students' mathematical achievement and beliefs are more similar to the textbook group. Also included are exploratory analyses of the pedagogical beliefs held by teachers before and after teaching in problem-centered classes, and those held by teachers in textbook-centered classes. The results of the student and teacher analyses are interpreted in light of research on children's construction of nonstandard algorithms and the nature of classroom environments.

Zemelman, Steve, Harvey Daniels and Arthur Hyde. 1998. *Best Practice: New Standards for Teaching and Learning In America's Schools,* 2nd ed. Portsmouth, NH: Heinemann.

This book summarizes standards of state-of-the-art teaching and practical descriptions of instructional excellence in six content areas. The authors dispel misconceptions and challenge time honored mathematics practices like memorizing facts; computing pages of sums, differences, products, and quotients; and memorizing rules and procedures for step-by-step proofs. They define the qualities of best practice and encourage teachers and principals to use manipulatives and models, encourage cooperative group work, have students write and talk about mathematics content, and teach using a problem solving approach. Best practice also involves moving away from teaching by telling, stressing memorization without understanding, teaching computation out of context, and testing for grades only.

Career and Vocational Education Standards

"More than half of our young people leave school without the knowledge or foundation required to find and hold a good job. These young people will pay a very high price. They face bleak prospects of dead end work interrupted only by periods of unemployment."

The SCANS report emphasizes that schools must teach a new set of skills so that young people entering the work force know how to identify and organize information and resources, relate well with others in work teams, and understand social and organizational systems.

SKILLS FOR THE 21ST CENTURY		
Basic Skills Reads, writes, performs arithmetic and mathematical operations, listens and speaks well	**Thinking Skills** Thinks critically, makes decisions, solves problems, visualizes, knows how to learn and reason	**Personal Qualities** Displays responsibility, self-esteem, sociability, self-management, integrity, and honesty
Reading locates, understands, and interprets written information in prose and in documents **Writing** communicates thoughts, ideas, information, and messages in writing, and creates documents such as letters, directions, manuals, reports, graphs, and flow charts **Arithmetic/Mathematics** performs basic computations and approaches practical problems by choosing appropriately from a variety of mathematical techniques **Listening** receives, attends to, interprets, and responds to verbal messages and other cues **Speaking** organizes ideas and communicates orally	**Creative Thinking** generates new ideas **Decision Making** specifies goals and constraints, generates alternatives, considers risks, evaluates and chooses best alternative **Problem Solving** recognizes problems, devises and implements a plan of action **Seeing Things in the Mind's Eye** organizes and processes symbols, pictures, graphs, objects, and other information **Knowing How to Learn** uses efficient learning techniques to acquire and apply new knowledge and skills **Reasoning** discovers a rule or principle underlying the relationship between two or more objects and applies it when solving a problem	**Responsibility** exerts a high level of effort and perseveres toward goal attainment **Self-Esteem** believes in own self-worth and maintains a positive view of self **Sociability** demonstrates understanding, friendliness, adaptability, empathy, and politeness in group settings **Self-Management** assesses self accurately, sets personal goals, monitors progress, and exhibits self-control **Integrity/Honesty** chooses ethical course of action

SCANS Report for America 2000—What Work Requires of Schools, Washington, DC: Secretary's Commission on Achieving Necessary Skills, U.S. Department of Labor, 1991.

Recommendations for Teaching Mathematics

Increase attention to

- Use of manipulative materials
- Cooperative group work and the discussion of mathematics
- Writing about mathematics
- Problem-solving approach to instruction
- Connecting mathematics to other subjects and everyday life
- Developing number and operation sense
- Thinking strategies for basic facts
- Describing, analyzing, evaluating, and making decisions about information
- Using assessment as an integral part of teaching
- Using multiple assessments, including written, oral, and demonstration formats

Decrease attention to

- Rote memorization of rules and formulas
- Single answers and single methods to find answers
- Use of drill worksheets
- Teaching by telling
- Practicing routine, one-step problems
- Doing fill-in-the-blank, yes-no, numerical responses
- Learning isolated topics
- Memorizing rules and procedures without understanding
- Using exercises or word problems requiring only one or two skills
- Using only written tests

Zemelman, Steven, Harvey Daniels, and Arthur Hyde. 1998. Best Practice: New Standards for Teaching and Learning in America's Schools, 2nd ed. Portsmouth, NH: Heinemann.

The NCTM Process Standards for School Mathematics

Problem solving is not a distinct topic, but a process that should permeate the study of mathematics and provide a context in which concepts and skills are learned.

—National Council for Teachers of Mathematics Curriculum Standards, 2000

Problem Solving
- Build new mathematical knowledge through problem solving
- Solve problems that arise in other contexts
- Apply and adapt a variety of appropriate strategies to solve problems
- Monitor and reflect on the process of mathematical problem solving

Reasoning & Proof
- Recognize reasoning and proofs as fundamental aspects of mathematics
- Make and investigate mathematical conjectures
- Develop and evaluate mathematical arguments and proofs
- Select and use various types of reasoning and methods of proof

Communication
- Organize and consolidate mathematical thinking through communication
- Communicate mathematical thinking coherently and clearly to peers, teachers, and others
- Analyze and evaluate mathematical thinking and strategies of others
- Use the language of mathematics to express mathematical ideas precisely

Connections
- Recognize and use connections among mathematical ideas
- Understand how mathematical ideas interconnect and build on one another to produce a coherent whole
- Recognize and apply mathematics in contexts outside of mathematics

Representation
- Create and use representations to organize, record, and communicate mathematical ideas
- Select, apply, and translate among mathematical representations to solve problems
- Use representations to model and interpret physical, social, and mathematical phenomena

The NCTM Content Standards for School Mathematics

Number & Operations
- Understand numbers, ways of representing numbers, relationships among numbers, and number systems
- Understand meanings of operations and how they relate to one another
- Compute fluently and make reasonable estimates

Algebra
- Understand patterns, relationships, and functions
- Represent and analyze mathematical situations and structures using algebraic symbols

Geometry
- Analyze characteristics and properties of two- and three-dimensional geometric shapes and develop mathematical arguments about geometric relationships
- Apply transformations and use symmetry to analyze mathematical situations
- Use visualization, spatial reasoning, and geometric modeling to solve problems

Measurement
- Understand measurable attributes of objects and the units, systems, and processes of measurement
- Apply appropriate techniques, tools, and formulas to describe measurements

Data Analysis & Probability
- Formulate questions that can be addressed with data and collect, organize, and display relevant data to answer them
- Select and use appropriate statistical methods to analyze data
- Develop and evaluate inferences and predictions that are based on data
- Understand and apply basic concepts of probability

Helping Your Child with Mathematics

Your fourth grader will be assigned Home Connections on a regular basis. Home Connections generally include a game or activity for you and your child to do together, along with a worksheet for your child to complete independently or with some assistance from you if needed. Each Home Connection is based on work students have done in class and includes detailed instructions. In addition to reading the instructions carefully, you can do the following things to help your child be successful with math.

Homework Help

1. If your child has trouble beginning to solve a problem, resist jumping in and explaining how you would do it. Instead, help your child build confidence in his or her own mathematical abilities by prompting him or her with questions like these:

- What is the problem asking?
- Have you seen a problem similar to this one before? How did you solve it? Could you use a similar approach to solve this problem?
- Could a sketch, diagram, or chart help you solve this problem? What kind and how?
- What is your plan for solving the problem?

2. If you can see that your child has arrived at an incorrect answer, try to help him or her discover his or her own mistake using questions like the ones below. When they retrace their steps or explain their thinking, students will often discover their own mistakes.

- Can you explain, step-by-step, how you solved the problem?
- Does this answer make sense to you? Why or why not?
- Your answer doesn't quite make sense to me. Can you prove that it is correct? How?

3. If your child easily finds the correct answer, you might ask him or her some of the following questions to extend his or her thinking and help improve communication skills. On the other hand, your child may be ready to move on to a more challenging problem.

- Can you explain how you know this answer is correct?
- Is there another way to solve this problem?

4. If you become confused when working with your child, try not to get frustrated or upset—confusion and mistakes are an important part of learning! We all feel confused at times when we're beginning to learn new things. Talk to your child about what you find confusing and try to work together to resolve that confusion. You might be able to clarify the issue yourselves. If not, ask your child to write a note on the homework about what you both found confusing, and encourage him or her to raise the question at an appropriate time during math class.

Math in Your Daily Life

1. We all use math, whether it's to halve a recipe or estimate what time dinner will be ready based on cooking times. When you find yourself using

Helping Your Child with Mathematics (cont.)

math, talk to your child about it and invite him or her to take part in it. For example, when you're picking up a few items at the grocery store, ask your child to help estimate the total cost of the items in your basket. These kinds of opportunities provide good practice, show that you value math, and demonstrate the ways in which math can be used outside of school.

2. Create fun opportunities to practice math by playing games together. Chess, checkers, card games, and a variety of age-appropriate board games help children develop problem solving strategies, practice basic facts, and consider probability in an informal way.

3. Jigsaw puzzles, blocks, and specialized puzzles like tangrams help students develop their spatial sense and apply geometric principles.

Attitudes about Math

1. Help your child see that math is an interesting topic and one in which we can all be successful. Express interest in what your child is doing in math class, and talk to your child about how he or she solves different math problems.

2. Getting the right answer isn't the only achievement worthy of praise: always praise your child for his or her hard work and improvements.

3. Model a positive attitude toward math. Even if you found mathematics difficult or frustrating when you were in school, try to avoid saying things like "Math is really hard" or "I never got math either." It's important for your child to know that like everyone else, he or she can be successful at math!

Grades 3–5 Competencies & Experiences page 1 of 6

Number Sense & Numeration		
Third Grade	**Fourth Grade**	**Fifth Grade**
Competencies		
• Read, write, order, model, compare, and identify place value of digits in whole numbers to 10,000. Use < and > symbols with whole numbers. Read and write tenths and hundredths as they relate to money. • Round whole numbers to the nearest 10 or 100. Know when an exact solution is required and when it's more appropriate to estimate. • Compose and decompose (e.g., put together and take apart) numbers to 10,000 by place value. Use expanded notation to represent numbers. (e.g., 3,206 = 3,000 + 200 + 6) • Locate and place whole numbers on a number line. • Understand, model, read, write, order, and compare common fractions (e.g., ½, ¼, ⅓, ⅙, and ⅛) using concrete models and visual representations. • Characterize numbers as odd or even in several ways. (e.g., divisible by 2, a double, a double and 1 more, etc.) Explain, demonstrate, and apply the fact that odd plus odd is even, and odd plus even is odd.	• Read, write, order, model, compare, and identify place value of digits in whole numbers to 1,000,000. Model, recognize, order, and compare common fractions (halves, thirds, fourths, fifths, sixths, eighths, tenths, twelfths, sixteenths) and decimals (tenths and hundredths). • Round 1-, 2-, or 3-digit whole numbers to the nearest 10, 100, and 1,000 for addition and subtraction problems and recognize which place (e.g., 1's, 10's, 100's, or 1,000's) will be the most helpful in estimating an answer. • Use a variety of physical and visual models to conceptualize fractions and interpret different meanings for fractions (e.g., equal parts of a unit whole, parts of a set, length, area, money, time). • Create, model, and recognize equivalent forms of common fractions and decimals to hundredths (e.g., 0.75 = ¾). • Locate common fractions and decimals to hundredths on a number line.	• Order, model, locate on a number line, and compare fractions, decimals (tenths, hundredths, thousandths), and commonly used percentages (10%, 25%, 50%, and 75%). • Round (with ranges from the nearest hundredth to the nearest ten-thousand) to estimate answers to calculations. • Demonstrate meanings for fractions in different contexts (area, set, number line) and recognize relationships between different forms such as mixed numbers, improper fractions, and decimals. • Create, model, and recognize equivalent forms of common fractions, decimals, and percents. (0.20 = ⅕; 0.20 = 20%; 20% = ⅕) • Explain prime and composite numbers, factors, and multiples.
Experiences		
• Explore different meanings for fractions (e.g., parts of a unit whole, parts of a set, length, area, money, time). • Explore equivalent fractions. • Explore fractions and decimals as two representations of the same quantities in the context of money (e.g., 50¢ is ½ of a dollar, 75¢ is ¾ of a dollar).	• Explore equivalent fractions and use equivalence to compare fractions. (e.g., ³⁄₆ = ½, so ²⁄₆ is less than ½) • Explore concepts of prime and composite numbers, factors, multiples, and negative numbers. • Explore fractions as quotients of whole numbers.	• Understand fractions as quotients of whole numbers.

Grades 3–5 Competencies & Experiences page 2 of 6

Computation

Third Grade	Fourth Grade	Fifth Grade
Competencies		
• Use strategies (e.g., doubles, neighbors) in the development and demonstration of computational fluency with addition and subtraction facts to 20. • Use models, words, and/or numbers to demonstrate the meaning of addition (joining two or more sets) and subtraction (taking away or finding the difference between two sets). Use the relationship between addition and subtraction (e.g., fact families) to solve problems. • Add and subtract up to 3-digit numbers with and without regrouping using models and a variety of efficient paper/pencil and mental strategies. • Use models, words, and/or numbers to demonstrate an understanding of multiplication and division as repeated addition/subtraction, fair shares, equal groups of objects, arrays, or skip counting. • Demonstrate computational fluency with multiplication facts up to 5 × 10. Develop and use strategies for multiplication facts up to 10 × 10. Use various strategies to multiply a 2-digit number by a 1-digit number. • Use estimation strategies such as rounding and front-end loading to solve problems and check the accuracy of the solutions. • Identify and apply the operation needed (addition, subtraction, multiplication, or division) for solving a problem. • Count, add, subtract, and estimate money amounts up to $10. Make change from $5. Use decimal notation to show money amounts to $10. • Use the calculator as a problem solving tool to investigate patterns, find the sum and difference of multiple 2- and 3-digit combinations, and find the average of a set of data.	• Add and subtract up to 4-digit numbers with and without regrouping using models and a variety of efficient paper/pencil and mental strategies. • Know and fluently use multiplication facts through 10 × 10. Develop efficient strategies for quickly determining division facts with divisors to 10 and dividends to 100. • Develop efficient ways to determine factors of whole numbers to 100 using an understanding of number relationships and models such as arrays. • Mentally add and subtract multiples of 10, 100, or 1000 to or from a number. Mentally multiply or divide multiples of 10 or 100 (e.g., 40 × 70 or 2700 ÷ 30). • Use different models of division such as grouping, sharing, and repeated subtraction to solve problems (including situations that involve remainders). • Multiply and divide 2- and 3-digit numbers by 1-digit numbers using a variety of concrete, visual, and paper/pencil methods. • Add and subtract commonly used fractions and decimals to hundredths using concrete models, money amounts, and visual representations. • Solve addition, subtraction, multiplication, and division story problems using a variety of efficient paper/pencil and mental strategies. • Select methods and tools (rounding, estimation, paper/pencil, calculator) appropriate to a particular context for operations with whole numbers. • Apply the commutative, associative, distributive, and identity properties to calculations with whole numbers.	• Use addition, column addition, and subtraction with multi-digit numbers (5 or more digits) in an efficient manner, making judicious use of mental strategies, estimation, rounding, and calculators. • Know and fluently use the multiplication and division facts through 12's, as well as factors and multiples through 144. • Multiply 2-digit by 2-digit numbers using a variety of efficient mental and paper/pencil strategies. • Multiply by powers of ten up to 1,000 to simplify calculations. • Divide 3-digit by 1- and 2-digit numbers with and without remainders using a variety of efficient mental and paper/pencil strategies. • Calculate and explain addition and subtraction of commonly used fractions and decimals to thousandths. • Describe, compare, choose, and accurately use strategies and operations for a variety of problem situations. • Identify the order of operations in a multistep problem. • Estimate the results of operations performed on whole numbers, fractions, and decimals, and use the estimate to determine the reasonableness of the final answer. • Apply the commutative, associative, distributive, and identity properties to calculations with whole numbers and decimals.
Experiences		
• Explore mental addition and subtraction of multiples of 10, 100, or 1000 to or from a number. • Explore the concept of division with and without remainders through solving story problems and creating multiplication/division fact families to go along with arrays. • Explore the commutative, associative, and distributive properties of multiplication, as well as the special properties of 0 and 1 in multiplication.	• Explore column addition with multi-digit numbers and addition, subtraction, and estimation with larger numbers (5 or more digits).	• Compute and perform multiplication and division of simple fractions, and apply these procedures to solve problem situations. • Use percent models (such as a Hundreds Grid) to interpret current events, news stories, and advertisements that relate to students' lives. • Determine common percentages of a number (e.g., 10%, 20%, 50%, 75%) and estimate percentages by rounding.

Grades 3–5 Competencies & Experiences page 3 of 6

Algebraic Thinking

Third Grade	Fourth Grade	Fifth Grade
Competencies		

Third Grade	Fourth Grade	Fifth Grade
• Sort a collection of objects by a variety of attributes and determine how a collection of objects has been sorted by examining evidence (e.g., a 2-circle Venn diagram level of complexity). • Describe, extend, and make verbal and written generalizations about numeric and geometric patterns to make predictions and solve problems (e.g., to figure out how many tile it takes to build the 10th arrangement of the pattern below—just add 10 three times and put one more in the middle). Arrangement 1 Arrangement 2 Arrangement 3 • Extend number patterns that involve adding or multiplying a single-digit number. (e.g., 4, 7, 10, 13… or 3, 6, 9, 12…) • Determine one quantity when given the other based on a simple relationship (e.g., using a T-chart to determine the number of wheels when given the total number of cars). cars | wheels 1 | 4 2 | 8 3 | 12 • Translate problem-solving situations into expressions and equations.	• Describe, extend, and make verbal and written generalizations about numeric and geometric patterns to make predictions and solve problems (e.g., If $2/8 = 1/4$ and $4/8 = 2/4$, then $6/8$ must equal $3/4$). • Extend number patterns with both whole numbers and decimals that grow by common differences, increasing differences, or simple multiples, such as doubling (e.g., 2, 4, 6, 8… or 1, 3, 6, 10… or 1, 2, 4, 8, 16…) • Represent and analyze patterns and functions using words, tables, graphs, or number sentences. • Create or complete a table of values given a specific rule. Describe the rule governing the relationship between two values in a table. (e.g., Every time you put a number in, it comes out with 3 more added on.) in | out 1 | 4 2 | 5 3 | 6 • Represent the idea of an unknown quantity or variable as a letter or symbol in an expression or equation. (e.g., $n + 6 = 9$) • Select appropriate operational and relational symbols to make an equation or inequality true (e.g. $15 \times 4 \ \square\ 10 \times 12$).	• Make generalizations about patterns that help solve problems (e.g., I know that the value of the 25th odd number is 49 because you just double the arrangement number and subtract 1 with odd numbers). • Identify, describe, and compare situations with constant or varying rates of change. • Represent and analyze patterns and functions using words, tables, graphs, or simple algebraic expressions. • Identify or describe a situation that may be modeled by a given graph (e.g., the growth of a plant over a 2-week period might be modeled by a line graph). • Identify and represent whole number data on the first quadrant of a coordinate grid. • Use letters, boxes, or other symbols to stand for unknown quantities in expressions or equations. (e.g., $98 \div n = 7$) • Represent and evaluate algebraic expressions involving a single variable. • Use order of operations (including parentheses) to solve problems.

Third Grade	Fourth Grade	Fifth Grade
Experiences		

Third Grade	Fourth Grade	Fifth Grade
• Explore the idea of selecting appropriate numbers to make an equation or inequality true. (e.g. $3 \times 4 = 2$ __ 6).	• Identify or describe a situation that may be modeled by a given graph (e.g., the growth of a plant over a 2-week period might be modeled by a line graph). • Explore situations that demonstrate constant or varying rates of change.	• Investigate how a change in one variable relates to a change in a second variable. • Supply a missing element in and explore possible rules that extend number patterns involving multiplication or division.

Grades 3–5 Competencies & Experiences

Data Analysis & Probability

Third Grade	Fourth Grade	Fifth Grade
Competencies		
• Read and interpret a wide variety of graphs, including graphs in which each division stands for more than 1 item. • Determine the mode and range of a set of data. • Collect, organize, and display the results of surveys or experiments by constructing line plots, bar graphs, line graphs, and/or pictographs. Label columns and rows and create appropriate titles for graphs. • Draw conclusions, make predictions, and draw inferences from tables, tally charts, pictographs, line graphs, pie graphs, bar graphs, and Venn diagrams. • Predict the likelihood of a particular outcome based on the initial conditions of a simple game or activity involving spinners, coins, or number cubes. Record and systematically keep track of the outcomes when an event is repeated many times.	• Read, interpret, and construct a wide variety of graphs, including bar, line, double line, line plots, pictographs, and circle (pie) graphs. • Determine the mode, median, and range of a set of data. • Devise and conduct surveys and experiments; systematically collect and record data; draw, support, and communicate conclusions based on data collected. • Predict and represent all possible outcomes for a simple probability situation in an organized way (e.g., tables, grids, tree diagrams). Solve simple counting problems. ("James has 3 pairs of pants and 4 shirts. How many different outfits can he wear?") • Predict the likelihood of an outcome prior to an experiment involving spinners, number cubes, or coins. Express the outcome of such experiments verbally and numerically using both whole numbers and fractions (e.g., 3 out of 4 or $\frac{3}{4}$), and compare predicted probability with the actual results. • Describe the probability of various outcomes or events using such terms as impossible, unlikely, somewhat likely, very likely, certain, and equally likely.	• Interpret and construct a wide variety of graphs, including bar, line, double line, circle graphs and first quadrant plots, as well as tables to display collected data and to provide evidence for conclusions. • Determine the mode, median, mean (average), and range of a set of data. • Compare two related sets of data using measures of variability (range) and central tendency (mean, median, and mode) using concrete materials, tables, and computation. • Compare different representations of the same data and evaluate how well each representation shows important aspects of the data. • Determine possible outcomes in a situation. Compare experimental probability to the theoretical probability of a particular outcome. • Analyze events or games of chance to determine the theoretical probability of an event occurring. Express that probability as a ratio (fraction or decimal).
Experiences		
• Investigate situations in which the more data one collects, the closer the actual outcome is to the predicted outcome. • Explore the median of a set of data. • Explore averaging problems by leveling off columns of cubes or base ten pieces. • Explore counting problems such as, "Sarah has 2 kinds of bread and 3 kinds of cheese. How many different kinds of sandwiches can she make?"	• Investigate the fact that probability cannot determine an individual outcome, but can be used to predict the likely frequency of an outcome. • Explore the concept and process of finding the mean (the average); develop a variety of strategies for estimating and finding the mean.	• Explore basic concepts of sampling, including the fact that larger samples yield better results and the need for representative samples.

Grades 3–5 Competencies & Experiences page 5 of 6

Measurement		
Third Grade	**Fourth Grade**	**Fifth Grade**
Competencies		

• Explain the need for using standard units, and select the most appropriate tool and unit to measure length, weight, capacity, and time.
• Identify the size of the most commonly used units of measure (e.g., inch, foot, yard, centimeter, meter, cup, quart, gallon, milliliter, liter, ounce, pound, gram, and kilogram) to make reasonable estimates. Select the unit that is most appropriate in a given situation.
• Develop strategies for determining the area and perimeter of a rectangle. Use models or sketches to demonstrate the fact that perimeter means the distance around something, while the area refers to the size of its surface.
• Tell time on digital and analog clocks to the minute and determine elapsed time in minutes and hours.
• Record time in digital form.
• Use a thermometer to determine the temperature in both degrees Celsius and degrees Fahrenheit.
• Apply the following equivalencies:
  ° 12 inches in 1 foot
  ° 3 feet in 1 yard
  ° 100 centimeters in 1 meter
  ° 4 cups in 1 quart
  ° 4 quarts in 1 gallon
  ° 60 minutes in 1 hour
  ° 24 hours in 1 day
	• Accurately measure length, perimeter, volume, and weight to the nearest metric unit and to the nearest U.S. customary quarter-unit (e.g., ¼ of an inch).
	• Carry out simple unit conversions within (but not between) metric and U.S. customary systems of measurement.
	• Make realistic estimates and measurements using most common units of measure (inch, foot, yard; cup, quart, gallon; ounce, pound; millimeter, centimeter, meter; milliliter, liter; gram, kilogram) and select the unit most appropriate for a given situation.
	• Relate the area of a rectangle and its dimensions to area models for multiplication and division.
	• Develop strategies for finding the perimeter and area of rectangles and related triangles and parallelograms.
	• Estimate temperatures and read thermometers in degrees Fahrenheit and Celsius.
	• Determine elapsed time requiring unit conversions (e.g., weeks to months, minutes to hours).
		• Select and accurately use appropriate units and tools for measuring length, weight, capacity, and temperature in both metric and U.S. customary systems.
		• Determine measurements of length and perimeter to the nearest quarter inch, nearest tenth centimeter and nearest tenth meter.
		• Develop and use formulas for determining the perimeter and area of rectangles and related triangles, parallelograms, polygons, and everyday objects.
		• Analyze the effects on area and perimeter of combining two simple geometric figures.
		• Estimate and measure the surface area and volume of a rectangular solid using square and cubic units.
		• Select appropriate tools to accurately measure, identify, and construct perpendicular and parallel lines, rectangles, triangles, and circles.
		• Use a protractor to measure angles up to 180 degrees and identify obtuse, acute, and right angles.
		• Add and subtract time amounts; convert time amounts from minutes to fractions of an hour and vice versa.

Experiences		
• Select and use benchmarks to estimate measurements (e.g., a "square corner" can be used to judge the size of other angles; a paperclip weighs about a gram). • Make estimates of length, weight, and capacity and then use the actual measurement to determine the reasonableness of the estimate. Develop precision in measuring objects and solving problems. • Estimate or determine the surface area and volume of solid figures by covering them with squares or by counting the number of cubes that would fill them.	• Develop strategies for estimating the perimeters, areas, and volumes of irregular shapes and rectangular solids. • Select and use benchmarks to estimate measurements (e.g., a "square corner" can be used to judge the size of other angles; a paperclip weighs about a gram). • Convert time amounts from minutes to fractions of an hour and vice versa. • Estimate and measure the surface area and volume of a rectangular solid using square and cubic units.	• Estimate conversions between customary and metric units. (e.g., one inch is about 2.5 centimeters, a liter is a little more than a quart) • Develop strategies for determining approximate volumes of irregular solids.

Grades 3–5 Competencies & Experiences page 6 of 6

Geometry

THIRD GRADE	FOURTH GRADE	FIFTH GRADE
Competencies		
• Recognize, describe, compare, and draw a variety of 2- and 3-dimensional shapes (e.g., pentagon, octagon, square, rectangle, cube). • Recognize 3-dimensional shapes (e.g., cubes, rectangular prisms, triangular prisms, spheres, pyramids, cones, and cylinders) in the environment. • Identify, describe, and classify a variety of 2- and 3-dimensional shapes (e.g., quadrilaterals, octagons, cubes, cylinders, spheres) using such terms as sides, angles, faces, edges, and vertices. • Combine and divide shapes in more than one way to create other shapes. • Create shapes with lines of symmetry using concrete models. Identify shapes that have line symmetry. • Develop an understanding of a variety of formal geometric terms, including face, edge, point, vertex, parallel, angles (right, acute, obtuse) and congruence. • Identify right angles in geometric figures or in appropriate objects, and determine whether other angles are greater than or less than a right angle. • Explore congruent figures. Recognize congruent and similar shapes.	• Identify, describe, and compare 2-D and 3-D geometrical shapes. Recognize congruent and similar shapes. • Identify, describe, compare, and classify triangles and quadrilaterals by attributes of their sides and angles. (e.g., An equilateral triangle has sides of equal length and angles of equal measure. A square is a rectangle with congruent sides.) • Identify line and rotational symmetry in 2-D shapes and designs. Build or draw shapes with line and/or rotational symmetry. • Model, sketch, draw, and label points, lines, line segments, angles, rays, various polygons, and parallel, perpendicular, and intersecting lines. • Identify right, acute, and obtuse angles in isolation and in geometric figures. • Understand angles as degrees of turn and make reasonable estimates of angle measures relative to 0, 90, and 180 degrees. • Predict and describe the results of performing reflections (flips), rotations (turns), and translations (slides) of polygons. • Locate and identify coordinates of points on grids, maps, globes, and other charts.	• Use properties of triangles and quadrilaterals to determine the lengths of their sides and perimeters, and to identify, describe, compare, and classify different types of triangles and quadrilaterals. • Develop, understand, and apply the following properties: the sum of the angle measures in a triangle is 180 degrees and the sum of the angle measures in a quadrilateral is 360 degrees. • Draw conclusions about the measures of corresponding sides and angles in two congruent or similar triangles or quadrilaterals. • Identify and build 3-dimensional objects from 2-dimensional representations. • Use measurement tools to accurately construct and label triangles, angles, and line segments. • Identify and describe line and rotational symmetry in 2- and 3-D shapes and designs. • Recognize congruent and similar shapes. Identify and describe a motion or series of motions that will show that two polygons are congruent. • Specify locations and describe spatial relationships and paths using coordinate geometry; find the distance between points along the horizontal and vertical lines of a coordinate system. • Identify the radius, diameter, and circumference of a circle.
Experiences		
• Describe paths for moving from one location to another on a grid. • Explore the effects on 2-D shapes of transformations (reflections, rotations, and translations). • Explore rotational symmetry.	• Identify and build 3-dimensional objects from 2-dimensional representations. • Explore the concept of congruence to draw conclusions about the measures of corresponding sides and angles of 2 quadrilaterals.	

NAME _____   DATE _____

Fourth Grade Math Skills & Concepts Student Report

Explanation of Color Coding

Pink: Just beginning to utilize this skill or concept

Green: Developing an understanding of this skill or concept

Yellow: Proficient with this skill or concept

EARLY FOURTH GRADE	LATE FOURTH GRADE	BEYOND FOURTH GRADE
Numbers & Numeration		
Reads, writes, and understands numbers to 99,999.	Reads, writes, and understands numbers to 1,000,000.	Reads, writes and understands numbers to 1,000,000.
Understands, models, reads, writes, orders and compares common fractions (e.g. ½, ⅓, ¼, ⅛, 1/16) using concrete models and visual representations.	Creates, models, and recognizes equivalent forms of common fractions and decimals to hundredths (e.g. ¾ = .75).	Demonstrates meanings for fractions in different contexts (area, set, number line) and recognizes relationships between different forms such as mixed numbers, improper fractions, and decimals.
Basic Facts		
Knows addition and subtraction facts to 20.		
Knows multiplication facts through 6 × 10.	Knows and fluently uses multiplication facts through 10 × 10. Developing efficient strategies for quickly determining division facts.	Knows and fluently uses multiplication and division facts through the 12's, as well as factors and multiples through 144.
Multi-Digit Computation		
Adds and subtracts up to 3-digit numbers with and without regrouping using models and a variety of efficient paper/pencil and mental strategies.	Adds and subtracts up to 4-digit numbers with and without regrouping using efficient paper/pencil and mental strategies.	Uses addition, column addition, and subtraction with multi-digit numbers (5 or more digits) in an efficient manner, making judicious use of mental strategies, estimation, rounding, and calculators.
Developing strategies to multiply 2- and 3-digit numbers by 1-digit numbers, including the use of multiples of 10 or 100 (e.g. 10 × 4 = 40, 20 × 4 = 80, 200 × 4 = 800).	Multiplies and divides 2- and 3-digit numbers by 1-digit numbers, using a variety of concrete, visual, and paper/pencil methods.	Multiplies 2-digit by 2-digit numbers and divides 3-digit by 1- and 2-digit numbers with and without remainders using a variety of efficient mental and paper/pencil strategies.
Story Problems		
Poses and solves addition, subtraction, multiplication, and division story problems using a variety of efficient paper/pencil and mental strategies.	Poses and solves multi-step story problems involving addition, subtraction, multiplication, and division using a variety of efficient paper/pencil and mental strategies.	Describes, compares, chooses and accurately uses strategies and operations for a variety of problem situations.
Algebraic Thinking		
Describes, extends, and makes verbal and written generalizations about numeric and geometric patterns to make predictions and solve problems.	Represents and analyzes patterns and functions using words, tables, graphs, or number sentences.	Represents and analyzes patterns and functions using words, tables, graphs, or simple algebraic expressions.
Geometry		
Identifies right angles in geometric figures or in appropriate objects and determines whether other angles are greater than or less than a right angle.	Identifies right, acute, and obtuse angles in isolation and in geometric figures.	Draws conclusions about the measures of corresponding sides and angles in two congruent or similar triangles or quadrilaterals.
Creates shapes with lines of symmetry using concrete models. Identifies shapes that have line symmetry.	Identifies line and rotational symmetry in 2-dimensional shapes and designs. Builds or draws shapes with line and/or rotational symmetry.	Identifies and describes line and rotational symmetry in 2- and 3-dimensional shapes and designs.

Fourth Grade Math Skills & Concepts Student Report (cont.)

EARLY FOURTH GRADE	LATE FOURTH GRADE	BEYOND FOURTH GRADE
Geometry (cont.)		
Recognizes, describes, compares, and draws a variety of 2- and 3-dimensional shapes (e.g. pentagon, octagon, square, rectangle, cube).	Describes, compares, and analyzes 2- and 3-dimensional shapes both singly and in relation to one another. Uses a variety of geometric terms including face, edge, point, vertex, parallel, perpendicular, and congruent.	Uses properties of triangles and quadrilaterals to determine the lengths of their sides and perimeters, and to identify, describe, compare, and classify different types of triangles and quadrilaterals.
Measurement		
Identifies the size of the most commonly used units (inch, foot, yard; centimeter, meter; cup, quart, and gallon) to make reasonable estimates and measurements. Selects the unit and tool that is most appropriate in a given situation.	Makes realistic estimates and measurements using most common units of measure (inch, foot, yard; cup, quart, gallon; ounce, pound; centimeter, meter; milliliter, liter; gram, kilogram) and selects the unit and tool most appropriate for a given situation.	Selects and accurately uses appropriate units and tools for measuring length, perimeter, weight, and capacity in both metric and U.S. customary systems. Determines measurements of length and perimeter to the nearest tenth centimeter and nearest tenth meter.
Develops strategies for determining the area and perimeter of a rectangle. Uses models or sketches to demonstrate the fact that perimeter means the distance around something, while the area refers to the size of its surface.	Develops strategies for finding the perimeter and area of rectangles and related triangles and parallelograms.	Develops and uses formulas for determining the perimeter and area of rectangles and related triangles and parallelograms.
Telling Time & Determining Elapsed Time		
Tells time on digital and analog clocks to the minute and determines elapsed time in minutes and hours.	Determines elapsed time requiring unit conversions (e.g., weeks to months, minutes to hours).	Uses time fractions as operants, and then converts back to whole numbers (e.g., $1\frac{1}{4} + 1\frac{1}{4}$ hours = $2\frac{1}{2}$ hours, and $2\frac{1}{2}$ hours = 150 minutes).
Data Analysis		
Reads and interprets bar graphs, line plots, and pictographs, including displays in which each division stands for more than 1 item.	Reads, interprets, and constructs properly labeled tables, bar graphs, line plots, pictographs, circle graphs, and line graphs. Is able to use these displays to find the mode, median, and range of a data set, as well as to draw, support, and communicate conclusions.	Is able to read, interpret, and construct a wide variety of well-labeled graphic displays, and can use such displays to find the mode, median, mean, and range of a data set, as well as to draw, support, and communicate conclusions.
Probability		
Predicts the likelihood of a particular outcome based on the initial conditions of a simple game or activity involving spinners, coins, or number cubes. Records and systematically keeps track of the outcomes when an event is repeated many times.	Expresses the outcomes of probability experiments verbally and numerically using both whole numbers and fractions (e.g., 3 out of 4 or $\frac{3}{4}$), and compares predicted probability with the actual results.	Determines all the possible outcomes of a situation in an organized manner, and expresses the probability of each numerically. Compares experimental probability to the theoretical probability of a particular outcome.
Problem Solving Strategies		
Uses several problem-solving strategies flexibly and fluently, including looking for a pattern, guess and check, using an organized list, and making a sketch or enacting the situation.	Develops and applies strategies to solve a wide variety of problems: verifies and interprets results with respect to the original problem. Developing the ability to remain engaged with a problem even when temporarily stuck.	Develops and applies strategies to solve a wide variety of problems; verifies and interprets results with respect to the original problem. Demonstrates patience and persistence in solving problems.

Fourth Grade Math Skills & Concepts Student Report (cont.)

EARLY FOURTH GRADE	LATE FOURTH GRADE	BEYOND FOURTH GRADE
Communication Skills		
Engages in pair sharing and class discussions using active listening and respectful behaviors. Understands the importance of listening to and learning from others' ideas.	Engages in pair sharing and group discussions and is able to elaborate on or paraphrase the ideas of others. Is able to disagree with grace and ask meaningful questions to clarify understanding.	Engages in pair sharing and group discussions. Feels comfortable with disagreement or confusion and knows how to respectfully ask questions or challenge ideas. Accepts feedback from classmates or teacher as a learning opportunity instead of as a criticism.
Is able to explain and justify ideas and conclusions using labeled sketches, number sentences, and words.	Is able to revise written work to communicate ideas and conclusions more completely.	Communicates thinking and reasoning in a clear and coherent manner using mathematical language precisely.

Comments

_____

_____

_____

_____

_____

_____

_____

_____

_____

_____

_____

_____

_____

_____

_____

_____

_____

_____

_____

Math Skills & Concepts Tracking Chart Early Fourth Grade

EARLY FOURTH GRADE

Skills & Concepts	Primary Instruction		Assessment		Support
	Units	Number Corner	Informal Assessment	Formal Assessment	
Numbers & Numeration					
Reads, writes, and understands numbers to 99,999.	Unit 2, Sessions 3, 4	September Calendar Grid and Problem Solving / October Calendar Grid and Number Line / December Problem Solving and Number Line / January Number Line	NCSB pages 2, 3	Number Corner Baseline Assessment (Blackline NC A 1.3) / Number Corner Checkup 1 (Blackline NC A 2.2) / Number Corner Checkup 2 (Blackline NC A 5.3) / Unit 1, Session 7	Number Corner Support Activities 2, 26, 27 / Additional time with December and January Number Line Games
Understands, models, reads, writes, orders, and compares common fractions (e.g., $\frac{1}{2}$, $\frac{1}{3}$, $\frac{1}{4}$, $\frac{1}{8}$, $\frac{1}{16}$) using concrete models and visual representations.	Unit 3, Sessions 1–11	October–December Calendar Collector	NCSB pages 42, 45 / BSB pages 47–49, 53 / Work Places 3A, 3B, 3C / WPSB pages 35–36, 38, 42–44	Number Corner Baseline Assessment (Blackline NC A 1.4) / Number Corner Checkup 2 (Blackline NC A 5.4) / Unit 1, Session 7 / Unit 3, Sessions 2, 20	Additional time with Work Places 3A, 3B, 3C / Number Corner Support Activities 24, 25
Basic Facts					
Knows addition and subtraction facts to 20.				Number Corner Baseline Assessment (Blackline NC A 1.1) / Number Corner Checkup 1 (Blackline NC A 2.1)	Number Corner Support Activity 1 (Also see Grade 3 Support Activities 1–6)
Knows multiplication facts through 6 × 10.	Unit 1, Sessions 8–17	September–January Number Line / October–January Computational Fluency	NCSB pages 6, 7, 9, 10, 12, 13, 15, 16, 22, 23, 25, 26 28, 29, 34, 35, 50 / BSB pages 6, 14, 15, 18 / Work Places 1A, 1B / WPSB pages 6–8, 10–13	Number Corner Baseline Assessment (Blackline NC A 1.2) / Number Corner Checkup 1 (Blackline NC A 2.3) / Number Corner Checkup 2 (Blackline NC A 5.1) / Unit 1, Sessions 2, 7, 21 / Unit 2, Sessions 5, 21 / Work Samples Unit 1, Sessions 4, 8, 10	Additional time with Work Places 1A, 1B / Number Corner Support Activities 12–17

NCSB—Number Corner Student Book, BSB—Bridges Student Book, WPSB—Work Place Student Book

Math Skills & Concepts Tracking Chart Early Fourth Grade (cont.)

EARLY FOURTH GRADE

Skills & Concepts	Primary Instruction		Assessment		Support
	Units	Number Corner	Informal Assessment	Formal Assessment	
Multi-Digit Computation					
Adds and subtracts up to 3-digit numbers with and without regrouping using models and a variety of efficient paper/pencil and mental strategies.	Not addressed at this time in unit work.	October Problem Solving December Number Line	NCSB pages 8, 11, 14, 17, 36, 39, 42, 46	Number Corner Baseline Assessment (Blackline NC A 1.3 and 1.5) Number Corner Checkup 1 (Blackline NC A 2.4) Number Corner Checkup 2 (Blackline NC A 5.3) Unit 4, Sessions 3, 21	Number Corner Support Activities 3–9, 18–20
Developing strategies to multiply 2- and 3-digit numbers by 1-digit numbers, including the use of multiples of 10 or 100 (e.g., $10 \times 4 = 40$, $20 \times 4 = 80$, $200 \times 4 = 800$).	Unit 2, Sessions 6–20	November and January Problem Solving	NCSB pages 24, 42, 46, 60 BSB pages 31–45 Work Places 2A, 2B WPSB pages 16–18, 21–23	Number Corner Baseline Assessment (Blackline NC A 1.4) Number Corner Checkup 2 (Blackline NC A 5.3) Unit 1, Session 7 Unit 2, Sessions 5, 21 Unit 3, Session 2 Work Samples Unit 2, Sessions 14, 18, 19	Additional time with Work Places 2A, 2B Number Corner Support Activity 22
Story Problems					
Poses and solves addition, subtraction, multiplication, and division story problems using a variety of efficient paper/pencil and mental strategies.	Unit 1, Session 10 Unit 2, Sessions 6–20 Unit 3, Sessions 9, 12, 13, 17, 18	October–December Problem Solving	NCSB pages 8, 11 14, 17, 24, 27, 30, 33, 36, 39, 42, 46, 56, 58, 60 BSB pages 31–33, 38–45, 54–56	Number Corner Baseline Assessment (Blackline NC A 1.5) Unit 1, Sessions 2, 7, 21 Unit 2, Session 5, 21 Unit 3, Sessions 2, 20 Work Samples Unit 1, Sessions 8, 10 Work Samples Unit 2, Sessions 14, 18, 19 Work Samples Unit 3, Sessions 13, 17	

NCSB—Number Corner Student Book, BSB—Bridges Student Book, WPSB—Work Place Student Book

Math Skills & Concepts Tracking Chart Early Fourth Grade (cont.)

EARLY FOURTH GRADE

Skills & Concepts	Primary Instruction		Assessment		Support
	Units	Number Corner	Informal Assessment	Formal Assessment	
Algebraic Thinking					
Describes, extends, and makes verbal and written generalizations about numeric and geometric patterns to make predictions and solve problems.	Unit 1, Sessions 11–13, 18, 19 Unit 2, Sessions 1, 2, 4	September–January Calendar Grid September–December Calendar Collector October Number Line January Problem Solving	NCSB pages 18, 19, 43–48, 56	No formal assessments at this time.	
Geometry					
Identifies right angles in geometric figures or in appropriate objects and determines whether other angles are greater than or less than a right angle.	Unit 1, Sessions 2, 3 Unit 4, Sessions 1–3, 12, 13	November Calendar Grid	BSB pages 61, 62 Work Place 4A WPSB pages 54, 55	Unit 4, Sessions 3, 21	Additional time with Work Place 4A
Creates shapes with lines of symmetry using concrete models. Identifies shapes that have line symmetry.	Unit 1, Sessions 2, 3 Unit 3, Session 1 Unit 4, Sessions 5, 8–13	Not addressed at this time in the Number Corner.	BSB page 77 Work Place 4C WPSB pages 67–70	Unit 4, Sessions 3, 21 Work Samples Unit 4, Sessions 5, 8	Additional time with Work Place 4C
Recognizes, describes, compares, and draws a variety of 2- and 3-dimensional shapes (e.g., pentagon, octagon, square, rectangle, cube).	Unit 1, Sessions 2, 3 Unit 4, Sessions 1–21	November Calendar Grid	BSB pages 65, 78 Work Places 4A, 4B, 4C, 4D WPSB pages 54, 55, 67–70, 74, 75	Unit 1, Sessions 2, 21 Unit 4, Sessions 3, 21 Work Samples Unit 4, Sessions 5, 7, 8	Additional time with Work Places 4A, 4B, 4C, 4D

NCSB—Number Corner Student Book, BSB—Bridges Student Book, WPSB—Work Place Student Book

Math Skills & Concepts Tracking Chart Early Fourth Grade (cont.)

Skills & Concepts	Primary Instruction		Assessment		Support
	Units	Number Corner	Informal Assessment	Formal Assessment	
EARLY FOURTH GRADE					
Measurement					
Identifies the size of the most commonly used units (inch, foot, yard; centimeter, meter; cup, quart, and gallon) to make reasonable estimates and measurements. Selects the unit and tool that is most appropriate in a given situation.	Unit 2, Sessions 3–5, 19, 20 Unit 3, Sessions 3, 10, 11 Unit 4, Session 15	September–November Calendar Collector	NCSB pages 4, 20, 21, 27, 30, 33 BSB pages 30, 81 Work Place 3B WPSB page 38	Number Corner Checkup 1 (Blackline NC A 2.2) Number Corner Checkup 2 (Blackline NC A 5.2) Unit 2, Sessions 5, 21	Additional time with Work Place 3B
Develops strategies for determining the area and perimeter of a rectangle. Uses models or sketches to demonstrate the fact that perimeter means the distance around something, while the area refers to the size of its surface.	Unit 1, Sessions 6, 18–20 Unit 2, Session 3 Unit 4, Sessions 10, 11, 16, 18	January Problem Solving	NCSB pages 55, 56, 60 BSB pages 7, 22–27 Work Place 4B	Number Corner Checkup 2 (Blackline NC A 5.2) Unit 1, Sessions 7, 21 Unit 2, Sessions 5, 21 Work Sample Unit 1, Session 4 Work Samples Unit 4, Sessions 16, 18	Additional time with Work Place 4B Number Corner Support Activity 21
Telling Time & Determining Elapsed Time					
Tells time on digital and analog clocks to the minute and determines elapsed time in minutes and hours.	Unit 3, Session 9	January Calendar Grid and Problem Solving	NCSB pages 47, 48, 56–58, 60 BSB page 53	Number Corner Baseline Assessment (Blackline NC A 1.5) Number Corner Checkup 2 (Blackline NC A 5.2)	Number Corner Support Activities 11, 12
Data Analysis					
Reads and interprets bar graphs, line plots, and pictographs, including displays in which each division stands for more than 1 item.	Not addressed at this time in unit work.	January Calendar Collector	NCSB pages 49, 59	No formal assessments at this time.	

NCSB—Number Corner Student Book, BSB—Bridges Student Book, WPSB—Work Place Student Book

Math Skills & Concepts Tracking Chart Early Fourth Grade (cont.)

EARLY FOURTH GRADE

| Skills & Concepts | Primary Instruction | | Assessment | | Support |
	Units	Number Corner	Informal Assessment	Formal Assessment	
Probability					
Predicts the likelihood of a particular outcome based on the initial conditions of a simple game or activity involving spinners, coins, or dice. Records and systematically keeps track of the outcomes when an event is repeated many times.	Not addressed at this time in unit work.	January Calendar Collector	NCSB pages 49, 59	No formal assessments at this time.	
Problem-Solving Strategies					
Uses several problem solving strategies flexibly and fluently, including looking for a pattern, guess and check, using an organized list, and making a sketch or enacting the situation.	Unit 2, Sessions 19, 20	October–January Problem Solving	NCSB pages 8, 11, 14, 17, 24, 27, 30, 36, 39, 42, 46, 55, 56, 60	Work Samples Unit 2, Sessions 14, 18, 19 Work Samples Unit 3, Sessions 13, 17	
Communication Skills					
Engages in pair sharing and class discussions using active listening and respectful behaviors. Understands the importance of listening to and learning from others' ideas.	Units 1–4, all sessions	September–January Calendar Grid, Calendar Collector, Computational Fluency, Number Line, and Problem Solving	Observations of students during all sessions and all Number Corner workouts	No formal assessments.	
Is able to explain and justify ideas and conclusions using labeled sketches, number sentences, and words.	Units 1–4, all sessions that involve written work	October–January Problem Solving	NCSB pages 8, 11, 14, 17–21, 24, 27, 30, 33, 36, 39, 42, 44, 46, 56, 58, 60	Unit 1, Sessions 2, 7, 21 Unit 2, Sessions 5, 21 Unit 3, Sessions 2, 20 Unit 4, Sessions 3, 21 Work Samples Unit 1, Sessions 4, 10 Work Samples Unit 2, Sessions 14, 18, 19 Work Samples Unit 3, Sessions 13, 17 Work Samples Unit 4, Sessions 7, 16, 18	

NCSB—Number Corner Student Book, BSB—Bridges Student Book, WPSB—Work Place Student Book

Math Skills & Concepts Tracking Chart Late Fourth Grade

LATE FOURTH GRADE

Skills & Concepts	Primary Instruction		Assessment		Support
	Units	Number Corner	Informal Assessment	Formal Assessment	
Number & Numeration					
Reads, writes, and understands numbers to 1,000,000.	Unit 6, Session 9	Not addressed at this time in Number Corner.		Number Corner Checkup 4 (Blackline NC A 9.4)	Number Corner Support Activities 2, 26, 27
Creates, models, and recognizes equivalent forms of common fractions and decimals to hundredths (e.g., $3/4 = 0.75$).	Unit 6, Sessions 2–21	March Calendar Grid, Problem Solving, and Number Line April Calendar Collector, Problem Solving, and Number Line May Number Line	NCSB pages 74–76, 78, 89, 93 BSB pages 123–125, 127–129, 139, 140, 146–147 Work Places 6A, 6B, 6C, 6D WPSB pages 79–81, 85–87, 89–91, 94–96	Number Corner Checkup 3 (Blackline NC A 7.4) Number Corner Checkup 4 (Blacklines NC A 9.3 and A 9.6) Unit 6, Sessions 1, 22 Work Samples, Unit 6, Sessions 4, 9, 10, 13, 17	Additional time with Work Places 3A, 3B, 3C, 6A, 6B, 6C, 6D Number Corner Support Activities 24, 25, 29 Additional Time with March–May Number Line games
Basic Facts					
Knows and fluently uses multiplication facts through 10 × 10. Developing efficient strategies for quickly determining division facts.	Unit 5, Session 15 Unit 7, Sessions 7, 9–10	February Calendar Collector, Computational Fluency, and Number Line March Computational Fluency April and May Computational Fluency	NCSB pages 37, 38, 40, 41, 62, 65, 67, 100 BSB pages 116, 117, 119, 161 Work Places 7B, 7C WPSB pages 102, 103	Number Corner Checkup 3 (Blacklines NCA 7.1–7.3) Number Corner Checkup 4 (Blacklines NC A 9.1 and A 9.2) Work Sample Unit 7, Session 7	Additional time with Work Places 1A, 1B, 3D, 3E, 7B, 7C Number Corner Support Activities 12–17 and 23 Additional time with April and May Computational Fluency games
Multi-Digit Computation					
Adds and subtracts up to 4-digit numbers with and without regrouping using efficient paper/pencil and mental strategies.	Unit 6, Sessions 15–17	March and April Problem Solving May Calendar Collector and Problem Solving	NCSB pages 73, 82, 96, 97, 99, 104 BSB pages 146, 147 Work Places 6C, 6D WPSB pages 89–91, 94–96	Number Corner Checkup 3 (Blackline NC A 7.2) Number Corner Checkup 4 (Blackline NC A 9.3) Unit 6, Sessions 1, 22 Work Sample Unit 6, Session 17	Additional time with Work Places 6C, 6D Number Corner Support Activities 3–9 and 18–20
Multiplies and divides 2- and 3-digit numbers by 1-digit numbers, using a variety of concrete, visual, and paper/pencil methods.	Unit 3, Sessions 12–19 Unit 5, Session 7 Unit 7, Sessions 9–10 Unit 8, Sessions 8, 12, 14, 17, 18	February–May Problem Solving	NCSB pages 61, 64, 66, 70, 78, 82, 87, 89, 93, 99, 103, 105, 106 Work Places 7B, 7C WPSB pages 102, 103	Number Corner Checkup 2 (Blacklines NC A 5.3 and A 5.4) Number Corner Checkup 3 (Blacklines NC A 7.2 and A 7.3) Number Corner Checkup 4 (Blackline NC A 9.3) Unit 3, Sessions 2, 20 Work Samples Unit 8, Sessions 8, 18	Additional time with Work Places 2A, 2B, 3D, 3E, 7B, 7C Number Corner Support Activities 22, 23, 28

NCSB—Number Corner Student Book, BSB—Bridges Student Book, WPSB—Work Place Student Book

Math Skills & Concepts Tracking Chart Late Fourth Grade (cont.)

LATE FOURTH GRADE

Skills & Concepts	Primary Instruction		Assessment		Support
	Units	Number Corner	Informal Assessment	Formal Assessment	
Story Problems					
Poses and solves multi-step story problems involving addition, subtraction, multiplication, and division using a variety of efficient paper/pencil and mental strategies.	Unit 6, Sessions 10, 17, 21 Unit 8, Session 13	February–May Problem Solving	NCSB pages 61, 64, 66, 70, 73, 75, 78, 82, 87, 89, 93, 99, 100, 103–106 BSB pages 146, 147	Number Corner Checkup 3 (Blacklines NCA 7.2 and A 7.4) Unit 6, Sessions 1, 22 Work Samples Unit 6, Sessions 10, 17	
Algebraic Thinking					
Represents and analyzes patterns and functions using words, tables, graphs, or number sentences.	Unit 7, Sessions 1–14	February Calendar Grid, Problem Solving, and Number Line March–May Calendar Grid	NCSB pages 66, 68, 74, 75, 84, 102 BSB pages 156, 157, 159, 163	Unit 7, Sessions 4, 14 Work Samples Unit 7, Sessions 1, 3, 7, 13	Additional time with Work Places 7B, 7C
Geometry					
Identifies right, acute, and obtuse angles in isolation and in geometric figures.	Unit 4, Sessions 1–3, 12, 13 Unit 5, Session 14	April Calendar Grid	BSB pages 61, 62 Work Place 4A WPSB pages 54, 55	Unit 4, Sessions 3, 21	Additional time with Work Place 4A
Identifies line and rotational symmetry in 2-dimensional shapes and designs. Builds or draws shapes with line and/or rotational symmetry.	Unit 4, Sessions 5, 8–13	Not addressed at this time in the Number Corner.	BSB page 77 Work Place 4C WPSB pages 67–70	Unit 4, Sessions 3, 21 Work Samples Unit 4, Sessions 5, 8	Additional time with Work Place 4C
Describes, compares, and analyzes 2- and 3-dimensional shapes both singly and in relation to one another. Uses a variety of geometric terms including face, edge, point, vertex, parallel, perpendicular, and congruent.	Unit 4, Sessions 1–21 Unit 5, Sessions 12–14	April Calendar Grid	BSB pages 65, 78 Work Places 4A, 4B, 4C, 4D WPSB pages 54, 55, 67–70, 74, 75	Unit 4, Sessions 3, 21 Work Samples Unit 4, Sessions 5, 7, 8	Additional time with Work Places 4A, 4B, 4C, 4D

NCSB—Number Corner Student Book, BSB—Bridges Student Book, WPSB—Work Place Student Book

Math Skills & Concepts Tracking Chart Late Fourth Grade (cont.)

LATE FOURTH GRADE

Skills & Concepts	Primary Instruction		Assessment		Support
	Units	Number Corner	Informal Assessment	Formal Assessment	
Measurement					
Makes realistic estimates and measurements using most common units of measure (inch, foot, yard; cup, quart, gallon; ounce, pound; centimeter, meter, milliliter, liter; gram, kilogram) and selects the unit and tool most appropriate for a given situation.	Unit 5, Session 6 Unit 8, Sessions 2, 8, 12, 13, 15–18	March Calendar Collector	NCSB pages 105, 173 BSB pages 192, 193	Unit 8, Session 19 Work Sample Unit 8, Session 8	Additional time with Work Place 3B
Develops strategies for finding the perimeter and area of rectangles and related triangles and parallelograms.	Unit 4, Sessions 10, 11, 16, 18 Unit 6, Sessions 1–4	April Calendar Grid and Problem Solving	NCSB pages 84, 87, 91 BSB pages 122–129, 147	Number Corner Checkup 3 (Blackline NC A 7.3) Work Samples Unit 4, Sessions 16, 18 Work Samples Unit 6, Sessions 3, 4	Additional time with Work Place 4B Number Corner Support Activity 21
Telling Time & Determining Elapsed Time					
Determines elapsed time requiring unit conversions (e.g., weeks to months, minutes to hours).	Not addressed at this time in unit work.	May Calendar Grid	NCSB page 105		Number Corner Support Activities 10, 11
Data Analysis					
Reads, interprets, and constructs properly labeled tables, bar graphs, line plots, pictographs, circle graphs, and line graphs. Is able to use these displays to find the mode, median, and range of a data set, as well as to draw, support, and communicate conclusions.	Unit 5, Sessions 5, 7–9, 11, 13, 15 Unit 7, Sessions 2, 3, 6–8, 11–13 Unit 8, Sessions 3–7, 9–11, 14–18	February and March Calendar Collector March Problem Solving May Calendar Collector	NCSB pages 63, 69, 72, 77, 78, 107 BSB pages 99, 103, 104, 107, 108, 112, 113, 169, 173, 174, 176, 177, 197, 199	Number Corner Checkup 3 (Blacklines NC A 7.2 and A 7.3) Number Corner Checkup 4 (Blacklines NC A 9.4 and 9.5) Unit 5, Sessions 1, 18 Unit 6, Session 22 Unit 7, Sessions 4, 14 Unit 8, Sessions 1, 19 Work Sample Unit 5, Session 11 Work Samples Unit 7, Sessions 3, 11 Work Samples Unit 8, Sessions 6, 7, 18	

NCSB—Number Corner Student Book, BSB—Bridges Student Book, WPSB—Work Place Student Book

Math Skills & Concepts Tracking Chart Late Fourth Grade (cont.)

LATE FOURTH GRADE

Skills & Concepts	Primary Instruction		Assessment		Support
	Units	Number Corner	Informal Assessment	Formal Assessment	
Probability					
Expresses the outcomes of probability experiments verbally and numerically using both whole numbers and fractions (e.g., 3 out of 4 or ³⁄₄), and compares predicted probability with the actual results.	Unit 5, Sessions 1–18	February Calendar Collector	NCSB pages 63, 65, 69 BSB pages 97, 101, 105, 106, 112	Number Corner Checkup 3 (Blackline NC A 7.3) Number Corner Checkup 4 (Blackline NC A 9.5) Unit 5, Sessions 1, 18 Work Samples Unit 5, Sessions 4, 15, 17	
Problem Solving Strategies					
Develops and applies strategies to solve a wide variety of problems: verifies and interprets results with respect to the original problem. Developing the ability to remain engaged with a problem even when temporarily stuck.	Units 4–8, all sessions	February–May Problem Solving	NCSB pages 61, 64, 66, 68, 70, 73, 75, 78, 82, 87, 89, 91, 93, 99, 100, 102–106	Unit 5, Sessions 1, 18 Unit 6, Sessions 1, 22 Unit 7, Sessions 4, 14 Unit 8, Session 19	
Communication Skills					
Engages in pair sharing and group discussions and is able to elaborate on or paraphrase the ideas of others. Is able to disagree respectfully and ask meaningful questions to clarify understanding.	Units 4–8, all sessions	February–May Calendar Grid, Calendar Collector, Computational Fluency, Problem Solving, and Number Line	Observations of students during all sessions and all Number Corner workouts	No formal assessments.	
Is able to revise written work to communicate ideas and conclusions more completely.	Units 4–8, all sessions that involve written work	February–May Calendar Grid, Calendar Collector, Computational Fluency, Problem Solving, and Number Line	NCSB pages 61, 64, 66, 70, 73, 75, 78, 82, 87, 89, 93, 99, 100, 102–106		

NCSB—Number Corner Student Book, BSB—Bridges Student Book, WPSB—Work Place Student Book